New Junior Cycle
English Ordinary Level

Contents

Study Essentials

Completed
(✓)

Please note: There was no exam in 2021 and 2020 for English Ordinary Level.

Photographs in Edco sample papers: Alamy p155, p169; all other photos Shutterstock.com

Welcome to Junior Cycle English Studies
Guide to Better Grades

Ordinary Level

 Marks: 180

 **Time allowed:** 2 hours

For your Junior Cycle English course, you will sit a two-hour examination at the end of third year. The examination will be linked to what you have learned in second and third year and to the learning outcomes for final assessment (see page vi). In any given year, a selection of learning outcomes will be assessed.

There will be no set sections and no set number of questions.

Stimulus Material

You will be given some stimulus material (for example, a poem, an extract from a play or novel, a poster, the text of a talk, a screen shot from a website) and asked to complete some tasks.

Typically, these tasks will involve:

- Comprehending – reading for information; following an argument; summarising ideas; linking to other ideas; questioning and evaluating ideas.
- Reading to appreciate – reading and identifying the various ways writers and speakers enrich their language and engage their audience; identifying how writers and speakers use language for different purposes.
- Responding – a variety of creative or functional writing tasks arising from the stimulus material.

Responding to Studied Texts

As well as questions on the stimulus material you could be asked to write about the texts you studied for your English course. You will be expected to write in a way that shows you have the language to write about poems, novels, plays, films and multi-modal texts. You will use this language to show your appreciation of such things as: characters, setting, themes, story and action; as well as identifying and discussing key scenes and favourite images.

Writing for a Variety of Purposes

At different points on the examination paper, you could be asked to write in a particular form (for example, letter, diary, blog, review, story) for a given purpose. In fact, there could be a whole section given over to writing.

General Advice

Because there is no set format for the paper, YOU MUST READ ALL THE INSTRUCTIONS VERY CAREFULLY.

Look carefully at the marks allocated to each section and then to individual questions.

This rough guide will help you plan your time.

Do not spend more time on a question than it is worth.

5-mark question	3 minutes
10-mark question	6 minutes
15-mark question	10 minutes
20-mark question	12 minutes
25-mark question	15 minutes
30-mark question	20 minutes
40-mark question	25 minutes
50-mark question	30 minutes
60-mark question/section	40 minutes
70-mark question/section	45 minutes
80-mark question/section	50 minutes
90-mark question/section	55 minutes
100-mark question/section	60 minutes

Exam Hints and Tips

Advice on Reading

Always read a text twice before you begin to answer questions. To help you complete the tasks, keep in mind the intended audience for the text and the purpose for which it was written.

Read the instructions carefully. If a question asks for your opinion, make sure you explain your point-of-view and, if you can, find evidence in the passage to support it.

If you are asked a question and you are not sure about the answer, try to find clues in the text to help you.

Remember that handwriting, spelling and expression are important, so be as neat and as accurate as you can.

Advice on Writing

Read the question and the instructions carefully. These will determine what style of writing is appropriate to the task.

No matter what the purpose of your writing, do some rough work. This will enable you to try out ideas and make a plan.

You should make sure that the tone, style and language of your writing matches the purpose and the form. A letter to your school principal will be more formal than an email to your best friend.

Writing tasks give you an opportunity to show that you can write intelligently, fluently and with a clear sense of purpose, control and enjoyment.

Neat handwriting, correct spelling and punctuation and the appropriate use of paragraphs will enhance the experience of your reader.

Advice on Writing about Studied Texts

If you are asked to write about a text you have studied, be sure that you know the title of the text and the name of the author or, in the case of a film, the director.

For narrative texts, you need to know the story, and be familiar with the characters and their relationships. You also need to have some ideas on the writer's skill in telling the story, how they enrich the language of the text and how they engage their readers.

For poetry, make a list of topics and themes dealt with in the poems you have studied. Apart from knowing what a poem is about, you need to study the language of the poem and the techniques used by the poet to bring the poem to life, including such things as imagery and sound.

In writing about the texts you have studied, show the examiner that you have read the texts carefully and thought about them. Express your thoughts in a clear style, and present your ideas in a logical manner.

And finally

An examination is an opportunity for you to show what you can do and to share your love for English and the texts you have read. Write with energy and conviction!
Be clear! Be confident!

Tick each paper as you complete it and tick the sections on each paper.

Record the marks allocated per section and the recommended time.

Junior Cycle English OL	Marks	Time	2022	2019	2018	2017	SEC sample paper 1	Edco Sample A	Edco Sample B	Edco Sample C	Edco Sample D	Edco Sample E
Reading to Appreciate												
Reading to Understand												
Reading Comprehension												
Responding to Texts												
Responding to Studied Texts												
Responding Imaginatively												
Writing for a Variety of Purposes												
Exam Complete												

Junior Cycle English Studies
Grading of the Final Examination

Grade Range	%
Distinction	90 to 100
Higher Merit	75 but less than 90
Merit	55 but less than 75
Achieved	40 but less than 55
Partially Achieved	20 but less than 40
Not Graded	0 but less than 20

Source: State Examinations Commission, 2022.

Study Hub

Your free online guide to smarter study.

Visit
www.edco.ie/onlinestudyhub

Remember
- You must answer all sections.
- Pay attention to the marks allocated to each section.
- Plan your time.
- Read instructions carefully

Map Your Progress!

New Junior Cycle Learning Outcomes Explained

These are the learning outcomes upon which the final assessment will be based.

Strand: Oral Language

Engaging with oral language – students should be able to:

- Listen actively in order to interpret meaning, compare, evaluate effectiveness of, and respond to drama, poetry, media broadcasts, digital media, noting key ideas, style, tone, content and overall impact in a systematic way
- Demonstrate how register (language style), including grammar, text structure and word choice, varies with context and purpose in spoken texts

Strand: Reading

Engaging in reading – students should be able to:

- Read texts with fluency, understanding and competence, decoding groups of words/phrases and not just single words
- Read for a variety of purposes: learning, pleasure, research, comparison
- Use a wide range of reading comprehension strategies appropriate to texts, including digital texts: to retrieve information; to link to previous knowledge, follow a process or argument, summarise, link main ideas; to monitor their own understanding; to question, analyse, synthesise and evaluate
- Use an appropriate critical vocabulary while responding to literary texts
- Read their texts for understanding and appreciation of character, setting, story and action: to explore how and w characters develop, and to recognise the importance of setting and plot structure
- Select key moments from their texts and give thoughtful value judgements on the main character, a key scene, a favourite image from a film, a poem, a drama, a chapter, a media- or web-based event
- Read their texts to understand and appreciate language enrichment by examining an author's choice of words, the use and effect of simple figurative language, vocabulary and language patterns, and images, as appropriate to the text
- Identify, appreciate and compare the ways in which different literary, digital and visual genres and sub-genres shape texts and shape the reader's experience of them
- Identify and comment on features of English at word and sentence level using appropriate terminology, showing how such features contribute to overall effect
- Understand how word choice, syntax, grammar and text structure may vary with context and purpose
- Appreciate a variety of registers (language styles) and understand their use in the written context

Strand: Writing

Engaging in writing – students should be able to:

- Demonstrate their understanding that there is a clear purpose for all writing activities and be able to plan, draft, re-draft and edit their own writing as appropriate
- Write for a variety of purposes, for example to analyse, evaluate, imagine, explore, engage, amuse, narrate, inform, explain, argue, persuade, criticise, comment on what they have heard, viewed and read
- Write competently in a range of text forms, for example letter, report, multi-modal text, review, blog, using appropriate vocabulary, tone and a variety of styles to achieve a chosen purpose for different audiences
- Use editing skills continuously during the writing process to enhance meaning and impact: select vocabulary, reorder words, phrases and clauses, correct punctuation and spelling, reorder paragraphs, remodel, manage content
- Respond imaginatively in writing to their texts showing a critical appreciation of language, style and content, choice of words, language patterns, tone, images
- Write about the effectiveness of key moments from their texts commenting on characters, key scenes, favourite images from a film, a poem, a drama, a chapter, a media- or web-based event
- Engage in the writing process as a private, pleasurable and purposeful activity and using a personal voice as their individual style is thoughtfully developed over the years
- Use and apply their knowledge of language structures, for example sentence structure, paragraphing, grammar, to make their writing a richer experience for themselves and the reader

2022J002G1EL

2022

Coimisiún na Scrúduithe Stáit

State Examinations Commission

Junior Cycle Final Examination 2022

English

Ordinary Level

Wednesday 8 June   Morning 9:30 – 11:30

180 marks

Examination Number

Day and Month of Birth

For example, 3rd February is entered as 0302

Centre Stamp

The theme for this examination paper is
A World of Wonder

Instructions

There are **three** sections in this paper.

Section A	Communicating and Responding	45 marks	4 questions
Section B	Imagining and Creating	65 marks	4 questions
Section C	Reflecting on Reading	70 marks	6 questions

Answer all 14 questions.

The questions do not all carry equal marks. The number of marks for each question is stated at the top of the question.

You should spend about 30 minutes on Section A, 40 minutes on Section B and 45 minutes on Section C.

When answering on studied material, you must use texts in line with what is prescribed for 2022.

Write your answers in the spaces provided in this booklet. You may lose marks if you do not do so. You are not required to use all of the space provided. You should read each question in full before beginning your response.

Extra pages are provided if needed. Label any extra work clearly with the question number and part.

You may only use blue or black pen when writing your answers. Do not use pencil.

This examination booklet will be scanned and your work will be presented to an examiner on screen. Anything that you write outside of the answer areas may not be seen by the examiner.

Suggested time for Section A: 30 minutes

Read the following two messages from two famous authors, written to sixth class students leaving primary school. Answer the questions that follow.

Image © Diarmuid O'Brien

Image: © Annie O'Gorman

Message 1: Deirdre Sullivan

New beginnings are exciting, but also a little bit scary. And you're going to need a friend to get you through this. So my message to you is, be your own friend. I didn't always like who I was when I was a teenager and I wasn't always on my own side. And that's not to say you need to be your only friend, other people are wonderful. We need each other. But if you find that you are harder on yourself than you are on your friends, remember you are just as deserving of kindness and compassion as other people are.

You can push yourself and strive to do exciting, adventurous and wonderful things, but if there comes a time when you wish you were someone else, that you had a different sort of brain, or shape, I really want you to remember that you deserve kindness. You matter. And you don't have to "be" anything special or marvellous or fantastic to deserve kindness. You deserve it anyway.

You are a person and you have value. And I hope that you can carry that with you on your journey. I wish you well as you start secondary school, and on every journey life takes you on, during your time there and afterwards.

Message 2: Judi Curtin

When I was your age, I was very sweet and innocent, and the most trouble I was ever in was when I was caught reading a book under my desk when I was supposed to be practising my sewing. So a real rebel!

When I was 12, I had no idea where life was going to take me. I knew I wanted to be a writer but for a long time I wasn't confident enough to try that, so it's fair to say, I took the scenic route. I had lots of jobs in my life, including working in a pickle factory and working as a teacher. I was a tour guide and once I made silk dolls and tried to sell them. This last job was a complete disaster - I should have paid more attention in sewing class!

I'm sure some of you are raring to go, and dying to get on to secondary school, and maybe some of you are a little bit nervous and wish you could stay in sixth class forever - and that's ok.
This is a time of big change and change is exciting but it can be scary too. Remember though, it's always interesting.
I hope you go on to do wonderful things.
Good luck!

```
Optional rough work




```

Question 1   (10 marks)

(a)   What do you think is the most important piece of advice Deirdre Sullivan gives to her readers in **Message 1**? Explain your answer.

```







```

(b)   What do you learn about life from your reading of **Message 2**, by Judy Curtin?

```








```

Question 2   **(10 marks)**

Look at both messages again. Which one of the messages appeals to you most? Give reasons for your answer.

© Alan Nolan

Optional rough work

Question 3   **(10 marks)**

You have been asked to write four top-tips for students who are about to start first year in your school. Write your tips below, based on your own experience, and explain why you think that following these tips will help them to do well in school.

Optional rough work

Top Tip 1:

Top Tip 2:

Top Tip 3:

Top Tip 4:

Question 4 (15 marks)

In **Message 1**, Deirdre Sullivan says,

You can push yourself and strive to do exciting, adventurous and wonderful things…

Imagine you have had an exciting, adventurous and wonderful experience. You have to give a talk to your class about it. Write the talk you would give in which you try to capture what the experience was like for you. The experience can be real or imaginary.

Optional rough work

Additional Writing Space. Label all work clearly with the question number and part.

| **Section B** | **Imagining and Creating** | **65 marks** |

Suggested time for Section B: 40 minutes

Read the following extract from *The Strangeworlds Travel Agency* by L.D. Lapinski. In it, a young boy, looking for a game shop, accidentally enters an unusual travel agency. Answer the questions that follow.

L.D Lapinski

The Strangeworlds Travel Agency

There have always been places in our world where magic **gathers.** You can see it if you look close enough. You might see an ancient horse and cart passing down a modern high street, or a cobbled alleyway that people walk into, but never out of. You might see it in a person - someone who looks like they've stepped out of an old photograph. Or perhaps, someone whose bag seems to hover off the ground catches your eye in a coffee shop. And when you look again, they and their bag have disappeared.

And, occasionally, you see magic in shops. The Strangeworlds Travel Agency was very much like a magical shop should be. The leaded windows were dirty and cracked. There was peeling paint at the front door. The sign over the window was clearly painted in silky gold letters **embellished** with black against a ruby red background. Jonathan Mercer was working, sitting at the shop desk reading.

A shadow crossed in front of the large bay window. And then it passed again, this time **pausing** in the region of the front door. After a moment the door opened, scraping over the swollen floorboards, and a boy came in, curling not so much his lip as his **entire** face at the sight of the shop interior.

"Um.." the boy looked around. "This isn't Games Warehouse, is it?" The interest slipped from Jonathan's face like water vanishing through a sieve. "Isn't it? Whatever gave you that idea?" The boy pulled his phone out. "It's supposed to be here."

"Ah well then, if your phone says this is the place, it must be correct. Don't trust your own eyes, whatever you do," replied Jonathan.

"What sort of place is this? What am I supposed to see?" asked the boy. The travel agency had no posters of Disneyland or the Algarve or anywhere else you might have wanted to visit. There were a few globes and atlases, and then there were suitcases. They filled the entire wall. The shelves went from floor to ceiling, each suitcase snug in a niche of its own, its handle waiting to be grasped and pulled.

Jonathan **sighed**. "We're a travel agency," he said. Jonathan smiled, a smile full of secrets. The boy frowned. "What do *you* do then?" he asked Jonathan. Jonathan pushed his glasses up his nose and folded his hands. But he was saved the trouble of answering by the suitcase to his left springing open.

The boy shook his head, snapped his mouth shut and ran out of the door.

Question 5   (10 marks)

The following words in bold appear in the extract printed on pages 9 and 10. In the case of each word, show what the word means, as it is used in the passage, by placing a tick ✓ in the appropriate box. Tick **one** box only in each case.

(a) **Gathers**

comes together ☐

grows ☐

disappears ☐

(b) **Embellished**

falling apart ☐

decorated with ☐

growing bigger ☐

(c) **Pausing**

breathing ☐

stopping ☐

passing ☐

(d) **Entire**

funny ☐

angry ☐

whole ☐

(e) **Sighed**

breathed out ☐

shouted out loud ☐

laughed out loud ☐

Question 6   **(20 marks)**

(a)   *" There have always been places in our world where magic gathers."*
        Give one example the author uses in the first paragraph to show what she means by this.

```
┌──────────────────────────────────────────────────────────────────┐
│                                                                    │
│                                                                    │
│                                                                    │
│                                                                    │
│                                                                    │
└──────────────────────────────────────────────────────────────────┘
```

(b)   What was unusual about The Strangeworlds Travel Agency?

```
┌──────────────────────────────────────────────────────────────────┐
│                                                                    │
│                                                                    │
│                                                                    │
│                                                                    │
│                                                                    │
└──────────────────────────────────────────────────────────────────┘
```

(c)   Describe the boy's reaction when he enters the shop.

```
┌──────────────────────────────────────────────────────────────────┐
│                                                                    │
│                                                                    │
│                                                                    │
│                                                                    │
│                                                                    │
└──────────────────────────────────────────────────────────────────┘
```

(d)   What impression did you get of Jonathan's character, from your reading of the passage?

```
┌──────────────────────────────────────────────────────────────────┐
│                                                                    │
│                                                                    │
│                                                                    │
│                                                                    │
│                                                                    │
└──────────────────────────────────────────────────────────────────┘
```

Question 7 **(15 marks)**

"But he was saved the trouble of answering by the suitcase to his left springing open."

Imagine that the boy doesn't run out of the shop at the end of the extract. Write a passage, continuing the story, in which you reveal what you think happens next. You are not required to bring the story to an end.

Optional rough work

But he was saved the trouble of answering by the suitcase to his left springing open...

Question 8 (20 marks)

Read all parts of this question carefully before starting your answer.

(a) Name a character that you found interesting or unusual, from a play **or** film you studied.

Title of play or film:
Name of character:

Optional rough work

(b) Explain what made this character interesting or unusual for you. Use a key moment from the text to support your response.

```
┌──────────────────────────────────────────────────────────────────┐
│                                                                    │
│                                                                    │
│                                                                    │
│                                                                    │
└──────────────────────────────────────────────────────────────────┘
```

(c) Write a conversation between yourself and your chosen character. In this conversation you should share your views with him or her on something that he or she did in the play or film.

```
┌──────────────────────────────────────────────────────────────────┐
│                          Optional rough work                       │
│                                                                    │
│                                                                    │
│                                                                    │
│                                                                    │
│                                                                    │
└──────────────────────────────────────────────────────────────────┘
```

```
┌──────────────────────────────────────────────────────────────────┐
│                                                                    │
│                                                                    │
│                                                                    │
│                                                                    │
│                                                                    │
│                                                                    │
│                                                                    │
│                                                                    │
│                                                                    │
│                                                                    │
│                                                                    │
│                                                                    │
│                                                                    │
│                                                                    │
│                                                                    │
│                                                                    │
│                                                                    │
│                                                                    │
│                                                                    │
└──────────────────────────────────────────────────────────────────┘
```

Additional Writing Space. Label all work clearly with the question number and part.

Suggested time for Section C: 45 minutes

Question 9 (10 marks)

Look carefully at this token for World Book Day. Answer the questions below. Choose the correct answer by placing a tick ✓ in the appropriate box. Tick **one** box only in each case.

(a) According to the token what date was World Book Day?

March fifth ☐

February twenty-seventh ☐

March twenty-ninth ☐

(b) According to the token who sponsors World Book Day?

Lego ☐

National Book Tokens ☐

Local booksellers ☐

(c) What is the value of the World Book Day token?

One euro and fifty cent ☐

One hundred and fifty euro ☐

Ten euro and fifty cent ☐

(d) Where will you be going if you win the prize of a family trip?

The library ☐

The United Kingdom ☐

Denmark ☐

(e) If you don't choose to use the token to get €1.50 off a book, what can you exchange it for?

A set of pens and pencils ☐

Lego toys ☐

A World Book Day Book ☐

Question 10   **(15 marks)**

A film is being made of a novel you have studied and you have been asked to design a poster to advertise it. Describe in words the three images you would use for your poster for the film. Based on your reading of the novel, explain why you would use these images.

Title of novel:
Author:

Image 1:

Why I used it:

Image 2:

Why I used it:

Image 3:

Why I used it:

Question 11 (10 marks)

Choose a novel **or** film **or** play that you have studied and explain two things that you found interesting about the world your chosen text was set in. You may reuse a novel or film or play that you have already answered on in an earlier question.

Title of novel **or** film **or** play:

Optional rough work

Question 12 (10 marks)

Read the following poem by Eleanor Farjeon, then answer the questions that follow.

Books

What worlds of wonder are our books!
As one opens them and looks,
New ideas and people rise
In our fancies and our eyes.

The room we sit in melts away,
And we find ourselves at play
With someone who, before the end,
May become our chosen friend.

Or we sail along the page
To some other land or age.
Here's our body in the chair,
But our mind is over there.

Each book is a magic box
Which with a touch a child unlocks.
In between their outside covers
Books hold all things for their lovers.

(a) In stanza one, the poet uses alliteration. Write out the line with alliteration.

(b) What effect do books have on the reader, according to the poet in stanzas two and three?

(c)   Do you agree that, 'Each book is a magic box'? Explain your answer.

Question 13   **(15 marks)**

Choose a poem you have studied that had a powerful theme or message. You may not use the poem printed on this paper.

Title of poem:
Name of poet:

(a)   What was the powerful theme or message? Explain your answer.

Optional rough work

_____

(b) Choose an image from the poem that you think best helps you understand this theme or message. Explain why you have chosen this image.

_____

You have found an envelope with a short letter inside. On the front of the envelope are the words, *A World of Wonder!* The letter starts with the following sentence:

Dear Friend,
Now that you have found this letter, you will not believe what I am about to tell you...

Continue the letter.

```
Optional rough work
```

23

Additional Writing Space. Label all work clearly with the question number and part.

Additional Writing Space. Label all work clearly with the question number and part.

Additional Writing Space. Label all work clearly with the question number and part.

Acknowledgements

Images
Images on page 3: Diarmuid O'Brien, Annie O'Gorman
Image on page 5: Alan Nolan
Image on page 6: vectorstock.com
Image on page 7: dreamstime.com
Images on page 9: goodreads.co; www.booktopia.com.au
Image on page 12: oliverclark.com (adapted)
Image on page 16: World Book Day Ltd, 6 Bell Yard, London WC2A 2JR; kanturkcu.ie
Image on page 17: anfocal.ie
Image on page 20: chasingtheturtle-wordpress.com
Image on page 23: pinterest.com

Texts
Sullivan, Deirdre, published Irish Independent Magazine, 23/05/2020
Curtin, Judi, published Irish Independent Magazine, 23/05/2020
Lapinski, L.D., Orion Children's Books, Published by Hodder and Stoughton, 2020
Farjeon, Eleanor, Books, The Works 5, Paul Cookson, Macmillan Children's Books, 2006

Material may have been adapted, for the purpose of assessment, without the authors' prior consent

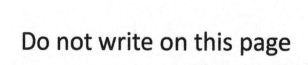

Do not write on this page

Junior Cycle Final Examination – Ordinary Level

English

Wednesday 8 June

Morning 9:30 – 11:30

2022J002G1EL2828

Coimisiún na Scrúduithe Stáit
State Examinations Commission

Junior Cycle Final Examination 2019

English

Ordinary Level

Wednesday 5 June – Morning 9:30 – 11:30

180 marks

Examination number					

Centre Stamp

The theme for this examination paper is
Respect

Instructions

There are **three** sections in this paper.

Section A	Reading to Understand	35 marks	5 questions
Section B	Responding to Texts	80 marks	5 questions
Section C	Reading & Writing for a Variety of Purposes	65 marks	5 questions

Answer all 15 questions.

The questions do not all carry equal marks. The number of marks for each question is stated at the top of the question.

You should spend about 35 minutes on Section A, 45 minutes on Section B and 35 minutes on Section C.

When answering on studied material, you must use texts in line with what is prescribed for 2019.

Write your answers in the spaces provided in this booklet. You may lose marks if you do not do so. You are not required to use all of the space provided. You should read each question in full before beginning your response.

Extra pages are provided if needed. Label any extra work clearly with the question number and part.

You may only use blue or black pen when writing your answers. Do not use pencil.

This examination booklet will be scanned and your work will be presented to an examiner on screen. Anything that you write outside of the answer areas may not be seen by the examiner.

Suggested time for Section A: 35 minutes

Read this speech carefully and answer the following questions based on it.

My name is Sinéad Burke. I am incredibly proud to be a little person. I have short arms and legs. I am 105 centimetres tall. My arms do not straighten fully, but I can lick my elbow. I'm not showing you that! (Laughter from audience)

I am lucky to have been born into a family that protected me from the unkindness of strangers, a family that gave me the strength, creativity and confidence that I needed. If you were to ask me why I am successful, I would say that it is because I was and I am a loved child.

Today I want to talk to you about how things are designed. I want to give you a new viewpoint. Yesterday I flew from Dublin to New York. The design of an airport offers very little independence when you're 105 centimetres tall, so I sat into a wheelchair and I was whisked through the airport by airline assistants. I don't normally need to use a wheelchair but the airport was not designed with me in mind. A wheelchair is the only way for me to get through it.

I stand at eye level with the baggage carousel. I'm not strong enough to lift my bag up on to it. Things like this take away my independence. But travelling on planes at this size isn't *all* bad. I never have to worry about leg room! (Laughter from audience)

I often forget that I'm a little person. Things like using a public bathroom remind me. It is an awful experience. I walk into the cubicle but I can't reach the lock on the door. I'm creative. I look around and see if there's a bin that I can turn upside down to stand on. *Is it safe?* Not really. *Is it hygienic?* Definitely not. If that doesn't work, I use my phone to push the lock closed. It gives me an additional four-to-six-inch reach.

Design also affects the clothes that I want to wear. I want clothes that show my personality. This is difficult to find in the children's department. I want shoes that reflect my age, and my professionalism. Instead, I'm offered runners with Velcro straps and light-up shoes. Now, I'm not *totally* opposed to light-up shoes! (Laughter from audience)

The way things are designed also affects my ability to do simple things, like sitting on a chair. I have to crawl on my hands and knees just to get onto a chair, whilst also being aware that it might tip over at any stage.

I drink far too much coffee. My order is a skinny vanilla latte; I'm trying to wean myself off the syrup! But the coffee shop is not designed well, at least not for me. They can't see me. "Next please!" they shout. The person next to me in the queue points to my existence and everyone is embarrassed.

I came here today to remind you that how things are designed affects people's lives, *all* people's lives. Being a designer of things like bathrooms and chairs is a big responsibility. So today, I want to ask you some questions. Who are we *not* designing for? How can we hear their voices and their experiences? I want you to open your eyes.
Thank you so much.

Optional rough work

Question 1 (5 marks)

From your reading of this passage, what do you think is the greatest day-to-day challenge faced by Sinéad Burke? Give a reason for your answer.

Question 2   **(5 marks)**

Which **one** of the following words best describes how you feel when you read this speech?

- Hopeful

   or

- Angry

Explain your answer.

Question 3 (5 marks)

Based on your reading of the last paragraph of this speech, what do you think is Sinéad Burke's message to people who design things? Explain your answer.

Question 4 (10 marks)

Did you enjoy this speech? Explain **two** reasons why you did or did not in your response.

2019

Question 5 (10 marks)

Your friend is going to deliver a speech to an audience of young people. Give **two** pieces of advice you would offer your friend on how to deliver the speech and explain why you think this advice would be useful.

Optional rough work

2019

Suggested time for Section B: 45 minutes

The following text is based on a letter received by fifth-class pupils in a primary school. It was from the manager of a book-publishing company. The class had written to the company because they were unhappy with parts of a schoolbook the company had published. Read the letter and answer the questions.

The Book Company,
Chapter House,
Library Lane,
Dublin.
27/6/18

Fifth-class pupils,
M.H.O.C. Primary School,
Dublin.

Dear fifth-class pupils,

Thank you for the letters you sent us about our book. In your letters you pointed out that women were not fairly **represented** in the careers section and that there were no pictures of people with disabilities shown in the book. We were very impressed with your research.

Because of your letters, we have reviewed the book and we agree with the **observations** that you made. As a result, when we update this book we will **ensure** that it will include more women working in different jobs. We will also make sure that the **illustrations** include people with disabilities and people from a wide range of cultures.

Once again, thank you all for taking the time to write to us. We always welcome **feedback** on our books, especially from the children who read them.

Yours faithfully,
Paige Turner.

Paige Turner
(Manager)
The Book Company

Question 6 (5 marks)

Which **one** of the following statements is false? Place a tick ✓ in **one** box only.

The students were concerned because the book had too many illustrations. ☐

The students were concerned because the book did not represent women fairly. ☐

The students were concerned because the book did not feature any disabled people. ☐

2019

Question 7 (10 marks)

The following words in bold appear in the letter printed on page ten. In the case of each word, show what the word means, as it is used in the passage, by placing a tick ✓ in the appropriate box. Tick **one** box only in each case.

(a) **Represented**

shown ☐

given ☐

gifted ☐

(b) **Observations**

things they forgot about ☐

things they remembered ☐

things they noticed ☐

(c) **Ensure**

make certain ☐

hopefully see ☐

carefully avoid ☐

(d) **Illustrations**

stories ☐

books ☐

pictures ☐

(e) **Feedback**

news about ☐

responses to ☐

donations to ☐

Question 8   **(10 marks)**

Is the letter on page 10 a formal letter or an informal letter? Give reasons for your answer.

Optional rough work

Question 9   **(15 marks)**

In her speech on page 4, Sinéad Burke says, "I want you to open your eyes." Write a letter to the principal of your school about an important issue in the school that you want to bring to his or her attention.

Optional rough work

Question 10   **(40 marks)**

Read all parts of the question carefully before starting your answer.

Optional rough work

(a) Name a character you liked from a novel **or** a play that you have studied.

Title of novel **or** play:
Name of character:

(b) Explain why you liked your chosen character. Use a key moment from the text to support your response.

_____

_____

_____

_____

(c) Name a character you disliked from a novel **or** a play that you have studied. You may choose this character from the same text or from a different text to the one you used in part **(a)** and part **(b)**.

Title of novel **or** play:
Name of character:

(d) Explain why you disliked your chosen character. Use a key moment from the text to support your response.

_____

_____

_____

_____

_____

_____

_____

_____

_____

_____

_____

_____

_____

_____

_____

(e) If **one** of your chosen characters, in either part **(b)** or part **(d)**, could make a wish at the time of the key moment, what do you think he or she would wish for and why?

(f) Choose **either** of the key moments you have referred to in part **(b)** or part **(d)** and explain how reading or watching this key moment made you feel.

Additional Writing Space. Label all work clearly with the question number and part.

Suggested time for Section C: 35 minutes

Advertisement A and **Advertisement B** show athletes from the 2012 London Paralympic Games. Study the advertisements carefully and answer the questions that follow.

Advertisement A

Advertisement B

Question 11 **(5 marks)**

In your view, what is the most important thing that **Advertisement A** tells you about the athletes? Explain your answer.

Question 12 **(5 marks)**

Which advertisement, **A** or **B**, is your favourite? Explain your choice. You may refer to the written text or the visual images, or both.

Question 13 (30 marks)

Read all parts of the question carefully before starting your answer.

(a) You have been asked to choose a poem you have studied that would be good to read out loud on a radio programme.

Title of poem:
Name of poet:

(b) Explain what your chosen poem is about.

(c) Why do you think your chosen poem would be good to read out loud on a radio programme? Explain your answer.

(d) Would you like to meet the poet who wrote the poem you have chosen? Give reasons for your answer.

Question 14 (5 marks)

Read the following sentence:

> The **unhappy clown** was shown no **respect**, so he **ran** away **quickly**.

Complete the table using each of the words in bold from the sentence above. The first example is completed for you. Use each word only **once**.

Pronoun	he
Noun 1	
Adjective	
Verb	
Adverb	
Noun 2	

Question 15   **(20 marks)**

Write the opening paragraph for a story called *'Show Me Some Respect'*. Your aim is to make your opening so appealing that readers would want to read on.

Optional rough work

Additional Writing Space. Label all work clearly with the question number and part.

Additional Writing Space. Label all work clearly with the question number and part.

Additional Writing Space. Label all work clearly with the question number and part.

Additional Writing Space. Label all work clearly with the question number and part.

2019

Acknowledgements

Images
Image on page 31: http://hghome.ie/dublin-game-changers-sinead-burke/ (11/2/19)
Image on page 34: https://i.ytimg.com/vi/avy0K_zNLU8/maxresdefault.jpg (12/2/19)
Image on page 36: http://www.e3ne.org/wp-content/uploads/2015/05/speech.jpg (10/1/19)
Images on page 38: https://www.depositphotos.com; adapted from image on https://www.unrestrictedstock.com (18/1/19)
Images on page 46: https://www.adweek.com; https://www.simonbutlercreative.com (18/1/19)
Image on page 48: https://senditrising.com/guest-ed-tyll-show/radio-mic-live/ (22/1/19)
Image on page 51: https://www.pinterest.ie/pin/131589620346823324/ (22/1/19)

Texts
Burke, Sinéad. *Transcript of Ted Talk.*
https://www.ted.com/talks/sinead_burke_why_design_should_include_everyone/transcript
Letter from Folens: Adapted from article in *'The Irish Examiner'*
https://www.irishexaminer.com/breakingnews/ireland/students-get-school-books-changed-after-highlighting-gender-and-race-inequality-851438.html (27/6/18)

Material may have been adapted, for the purpose of assessment, without the authors' prior consent.

Junior Cycle Final Examination – Ordinary Level

English

Wednesday 5 June
Morning 9:30 – 11:30

Coimisiún na Scrúduithe Stáit
State Examinations Commission

Junior Cycle 2018
Final Examination
English
Ordinary Level
Wednesday, 6 June – Morning 9:30 to 11:30
180 marks

Examination Number				

Centre Stamp

Cumulative total	
Note: The mark above must equal the mark awarded in the **Total** box.	

For the Examiner only			
Section	Question	Examiner	Adv.
A	1.		
	2.		
	3.		
	4.		
B	5.		
	6.		
	7.		
	8.		
C	9.		
	10.		
	11.		
	12.		
D	13.		
	14.		
Assessment Task	AT		
Total			

57

The theme for this examination paper is
Freedom

Instructions

There are four sections in this examination paper.

Section A	Responding to Poetry	40 marks	4 questions
Section B	Reading and Responding Imaginatively	65 marks	4 questions
Section C	Writing for a Variety of Purposes	40 marks	4 questions
Section D	Understanding Key Moments in Drama	35 marks	2 questions

Answer all 14 questions.

The questions do not all carry equal marks. The number of marks for each question is stated at the top of the question.

You should spend about 30 minutes on Section A, 35 minutes on Section B, 30 minutes on Section C and 20 minutes on Section D.

When answering on studied material, you must use texts in line with what is prescribed for 2018.

Write your answers in the spaces provided in this booklet. You may lose marks if you do not do so. You are not required to use all of the space provided. You should read each question in full before beginning your response.

Extra pages are provided if needed. Label any extra work clearly with the question number and part.

You may only use blue or black pen when writing your answers. Do not use pencil.

Section A	Responding to Poetry	40 marks

Suggested time for Section A: 30 minutes

Read this poem carefully and answer the following questions based on it.

Getting Dressed

Whose idea was it
And why do we all play along
pretending that having fun
is doing something wrong?

I watch my daughter dress at weekends
her five year old wardrobe grab.
She comes out of her bedroom
in a glittered dress and swimming cap
a pair of reindeered Christmas tights
star sunglasses on her beaming face

I'm in a plain t-shirt and jeans again.
I'm the caged* one.   * Trapped
She is sane.

By Hollie McNish

Question 1   **5 marks**

In the poem, what is the difference between the way that the poet dresses and the way that her daughter dresses?

_____

_____

_____

_____

_____

_____

_____

Question 2   **5 marks**

Why do you think the poet feels 'caged'? Explain your answer.

_____

_____

_____

_____

_____

_____

_____

Question 3   **10 marks**

Do you think that young people today are free to dress as they wish? Explain your point of view.

┌──┐
│   Optional rough work   │
│   │
│   │
│   │
│   │
│   │
└──┘

_____

_____

_____

_____

_____

_____

_____

_____

_____

_____

_____

_____

_____

_____

_____

_____

Question 4   **20 marks**

Choose a poem you have studied where the poet expresses a strong feeling about something he or she has experienced. You may not use the poem printed on this paper.

+---+
| Optional rough work |
| |
| |
| |
| |
| |
| |
+---+

(a)   Title of poem: _____

(b)   Name of poet: _____

(c)   What was the poet feeling?

_____

_____

(d)   Why do you think the poet was feeling that way?

_____

_____

_____

_____

_____

_____

_____

_____

_____

_____

(e) Did you think the poet had chosen a good title for his or her poem? Give a reason for your answer.

_____

_____

_____

_____

_____

_____

_____

_____

(f) Did you like or dislike the poem you have chosen? Explain your answer.

_____

_____

_____

_____

_____

_____

_____

_____

_____

Additional Writing Space. Label all work clearly with the question number and part.

Suggested time for Section B: 35 minutes

Read the following extract from Michael Morpurgo's short story, *I Believe in Unicorns* and answer the questions.

My name is Tomas Porec. I was seven years old when I first met the unicorn lady. I believed in unicorns then. I am nearly twenty now and because of her I still believe in unicorns.

My little town, hidden deep in its own valley, was an ordinary place. But when I was seven it was a place of magic and wonder to me. I tobogganed the slopes in winter and swam in the lake in the summer.

I never did like school though. It wasn't the school's fault, nor the teachers'. I longed always to be outside, running free up in the hills. I loved my free time. As soon as school was over, it was back home for some bread and honey – then off out to play.

But one afternoon my mother wanted to do some shopping in town and asked me to go with her. "I hate shopping," I told her.
"I know that, dear," she said. "That's why I'm taking you to the library. It'll be good for you. There's a new librarian and she tells stories after school. Everyone says she's brilliant."
My mother walked me up the steps into the library. "Be good," she said and she was gone.

I could see an excited huddle of children, jostling to get a better look at something. It was a unicorn, carved out of wood and painted white. He was so lifelike that if he'd got up and trotted off I wouldn't have been at all surprised. Beside the unicorn stood a lady with a smiling face, a bright flowery scarf around her shoulders. She sat down slowly on the unicorn, folded her hands in her lap and she told a story. I wanted to hear her, everyone did, because every word she spoke sounded true. After she had finished no one spoke.

Then a hand went up. It was a small boy from my school, Milos with the sticky-up hair. "Can I read a story, miss?" he asked. So, sitting on the unicorn he read us his story. One after another, they wanted their turn on the magical unicorn. I longed to have a go myself, but I didn't dare. I was afraid of making a fool of myself. The hour flew by.

One afternoon the unicorn lady took out from her bag a rather old and damaged-looking book, all charred at the edges. It was, she told us, her very own copy of *The Little Match Girl* by Hans Christian Andersen. "Why has it been burnt?" I asked her.

"This is the most precious book I have, Tomas," she said. "When I was very little there were wicked soldiers in my town who were frightened of the magic of stories, because stories make you think and dream; books make you want to ask questions. And they didn't want that. One night I was with my father watching them burn a great pile of books, when suddenly my father ran forward and plucked a book out of the bonfire. The soldiers beat him but he held on to the book and wouldn't let go of it. It was this book. Tomas, would you like to come and sit on the unicorn and read it to us?"

I had never been any good at reading out loud. But now, sitting on the magic unicorn, I heard my voice strong and loud. It was like singing a song. The words danced on the air and everyone listened.

Question 5   **20 marks**

Base your answers on the text printed above. Place a tick ✓ in the box beside the correct answer. Tick one box only in each case.

(a)   What age does the narrator Tomas tell the reader that he is now?

         nineteen   ☐

         twenty   ☐

         twenty-one   ☐

         thirty   ☐

(b)   Why did Tomas not like school?

         He didn't like reading.   ☐

         He always wanted to be outside. ☐

         He had no friends there.   ☐

         The teachers were not nice.   ☐

(c)   Which of the following statements is false?

Tomas's mother left him at the library because she thought it was good for him. ☐

Tomas's mother left him at the library because she wanted to go shopping. ☐

Tomas's mother left him at the library to do his homework. ☐

Tomas's mother left him at the library to hear the unicorn lady's stories. ☐

(d)   Why was Tomas frightened to read a story while sitting on the magic unicorn?

He was scared of the unicorn lady. ☐

He was afraid of making a fool of himself. ☐

He thought that storytelling was just for younger children. ☐

He was too busy tobogganing. ☐

Question 6   **10 marks**

Why do you think *The Little Match Girl* was the unicorn lady's most precious book? Explain your answer.

_____

_____

_____

_____

_____

_____

_____

_____

_____

_____

_____

_____

Question 7   **10 marks**

Tomas tells us that he loved his free time.   Explain how you like to spend your free time.

Optional rough work

_____

_____

_____

_____

_____

_____

_____

_____

_____

_____

_____

_____

_____

_____

_____

_____

_____

Question 8   **25 marks**

Read parts (c), (d), (e) and (f) below and then choose a novel or a short story you have studied.

(a)   Name of novel or short story: _____

(b)   Author: _____

Optional rough work

(c)   If you could ask a character from your chosen text an interesting question about something he or she did, what would the question be?

Name of character: _____

What is the interesting question you would ask?

_____

_____

_____

(d)   What answer do you think the character would give? You may answer as the character.

_____

_____

_____

_____

_____

_____

_____

_____

_____

(e) Would you like to have this character as a friend? Give a reason for your answer.

_____

_____

_____

_____

_____

_____

_____

_____

(f) If you could add a completely new character to the novel or short story you have chosen, what would that character be like and what would he or she do? Explain your answer.

_____

_____

_____

_____

_____

_____

_____

_____

_____

_____

_____

_____

2018

Additional Writing Space. Label all work clearly with the question number and part.

Suggested time for Section C: 30 minutes

Optional rough work

Question 9   **10 marks**

Study the advertisement for camping equipment shown above. Why do you think the phrase *ENJOY FREEDOM* is used in this advertisement? Explain your answer.

_____

_____

_____

_____

_____

_____

_____

_____

_____

_____

_____

_____

Question 10   **10 marks**

Picture A and Picture B show people enjoying two different types of freedom. Write a descriptive paragraph based on **one** of the two pictures below.

Picture A

Picture B

Optional rough work

Descriptive paragraph for Picture: ___

_____

_____

_____

_____

_____

_____

_____

_____

_____

_____

_____

_____

_____

_____

_____

_____

_____

You and your classmates are going to travel along part of *The Wild Atlantic Way** next weekend.
You all meet at break time to try to decide whether to camp or to stay in hotels. You know what
you would prefer to do. Write out the talk you would give to persuade your classmates to agree
with you.

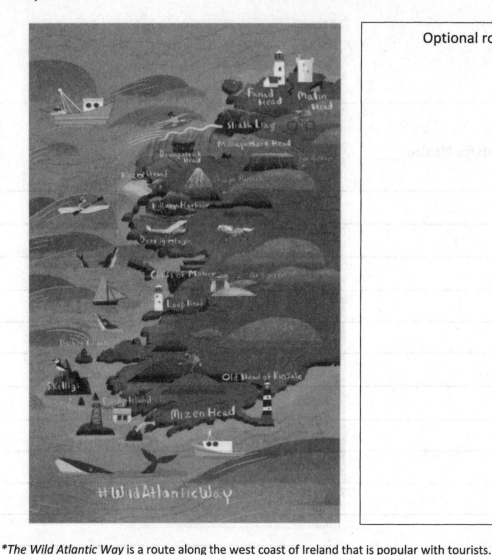

Optional rough work

The Wild Atlantic Way is a route along the west coast of Ireland that is popular with tourists.

_____

_____

_____

_____

_____

_____

_____

_____

_____

_____

_____

_____

_____

_____

_____

_____

_____

_____

_____

_____

_____

_____

Question 12   **5 marks**

Rewrite the following passage adding capital letters, full stops and inverted commas where necessary.

david walliams published his first book, The Boy in the Dress in 2008 Since then he has written many more books, some of which were illustrated by quentin blake

_____

_____

_____

_____

_____

_____

_____

_____

Additional Writing Space. Label all work clearly with the question number and part.

Section D   **Understanding Key Moments in Drama**   **35 marks**

Suggested time for Section D: 20 minutes

Question 13   **20 marks**

Choose a moment in a play you have studied when something important happens.

(a)   Title of play: _____

(b)   Name of playwright: _____

Optional rough work

(c)   What happens at your chosen moment? Give your answer in one sentence.

_____

_____

_____

(d)   Why is it important? Explain your answer.

_____

_____

_____

_____

_____

_____

(e) Imagine you are directing a performance of the play and you have the freedom to stage your chosen moment in any way you like. Explain what you would do to make the moment interesting for the audience.

Optional rough work

_____

_____

_____

_____

_____

_____

_____

_____

_____

_____

_____

_____

_____

_____

_____

_____

_____

_____

You are writing a play called '*Freedom*'. Write a conversation that takes place in the opening scene of the play, featuring the characters from **one** of the pictures below. In the conversation your characters should discuss how they would like to enjoy the freedom of summer.

Picture A	**Picture B**	**Picture C**

Optional rough work

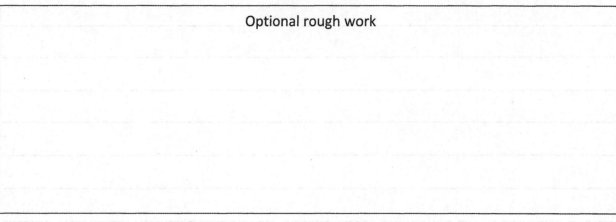

Conversation for picture: _____

_____

_____

_____

_____

_____

_____

_____

_____

Additional Writing Space. Label all work clearly with the question number and part.

Additional Writing Space. Label all work clearly with the question number and part.

Additional Writing Space. Label all work clearly with the question number and part.

Acknowledgements

Images

Image on page 59: www.mzayat.com

Image on page 64: www.natureworks.co.au

Image on page 67: www.brianpate.com

Image on page 71: www.adsoftheworld.com/media/outdoor/macpac_freedom

Images on page 72: www.saintsboardriders.co.uk, www.istockphoto.com

Image on page 74: www.pinterest.ie/tourireland/the-wild-atlantic-way/

Image on page 75: www.worldofdavidwalliams.com

Images on page 79: www.depositphoto.com, www.depositphoto.com, www.clipartlibrary.com

Texts

Morpurgo, Michael. *I Believe in Unicorns*. London: Walker Books, 2006.

McNish, Hollie. "Getting Dressed" www.holliepoetry.com (29/2/16)

Material may have been adapted, for the purpose of assessment, without the authors' prior consent.

Junior Cycle Final Examination – Ordinary Level

English

Wednesday 6 June

Morning 9:30 – 11:30

Coimisiún na Scrúduithe Stáit
State Examinations Commission

Junior Cycle 2017
Final Examination

English

Ordinary Level

Wednesday, 7 June – Morning 9:30 to 11:30

180 marks

Examination Number				

Centre Stamp

Instructions

There are four sections in this examination paper.

Section A	Reading and Responding Imaginatively	50 marks	3 questions
Section B	Appreciating Visual Genres	60 marks	5 questions
Section C	Choosing the Words and Tone to Use	35 marks	4 questions
Section D	Writing for a Variety of Purposes	35 marks	4 questions

Answer all sixteen questions.

The questions do not all carry equal marks. The number of marks for each question is stated at the top of the question.

You should spend about 30 minutes on Section A, 35 minutes on Section B, 20 minutes on Section C and 30 minutes on Section D.

When answering on studied material, you must use texts in line with what is prescribed for 2017.

Write your answers in the spaces provided in this booklet. You may lose marks if you do not do so. You are not required to use all of the space provided.

Extra pages are provided if needed. Label any extra work clearly with the question number and part.

Read the following extract from an interview with Irish film director John Carney.

In this interview Irish director John Carney talks about his latest film *Sing Street*, which tells the story of a Dublin teenager who forms a band in order to impress a girl.

What was your audition process like? What were you looking for?

I was looking for kids that had character. I wanted kids that had their own stories and were able to tell stories, all that sort of stuff, really. Apart from musical skill, which was important, most of all I was looking for kids who could make me laugh.

You've said this film is partly based on your own life. What was the biggest difference between your own life story and the story the film tells?

The biggest difference is that the main character, Conor, is an incredibly handsome kid who is so full of confidence. I wasn't like that at all. I had an inner belief in myself, but I didn't walk around with that swagger. I didn't look that way. As soon as Ferdia* got the part of Conor, the film changed. We decided to just go with the ridiculous confidence Ferdia has. He's hilarious. Kids nowadays have that sort of confidence.

*Ferdia – The actor who played the part of Conor in *Sing Street*.

You had huge success in 2007 with your earlier film 'Once'. Do you get tired of people always talking about that film?

No, I'm absolutely fine with that. It's the thing that's allowed me to make more films, and it's allowed me to travel, and it's allowed me to buy a house. *[Laughs]* It's allowed me to not worry every day about money. And as a creative person — that's a massive thing. Every painter and poet and artist and musician wonders, "Can I afford to continue to do this?" And *Once* is the thing that allows me to make films.

Did U2 have any involvement in the film, 'Sing Street'?

They were actually very helpful early on in the film. Bono and Edge were both really helpful in terms of pitching story ideas, and talking about bands in the '80s, and talking about youth. They set up the ultimate pop band, really, so I'd be a fool not to pick their brains. You know, I was in bands, but I wasn't in a successful band in the sense that U2 is successful. Bono could give us a good idea of what it's like to succeed as a band. Also, the point of my film is that these kids are in a good band. They do become good, and U2 did become good.

People keep comparing 'Sing Street' to another film about a Dublin band, 'The Commitments'. What do you think?

The Commitments and *Sing Street* couldn't be more different. In *The Commitments*, they're a cover band, doing cover versions of old soul songs – other people's songs. That's fine, and it's very funny and enjoyable. But we're telling the story of a creative process – of writing love songs to get the girl, to improve your life, to get off the island, and to be a success. *Sing Street* is set in Ireland, but in a sense it's a film about the American Dream – at the end Conor is punching the air and heading off to follow his dreams.

Question 1   **20 marks**
Base your answers on the text printed above. Place the correct letter in the box provided.

(a)   Why did the Dublin teenager in the film *Sing Street* form a band?

      A. To impress a girl
      B. To make money
      C. Because he was bored
      D. Because he liked U2

(b) When John Carney was auditioning actors for his film, what was he was looking for 'most of all'?

    A. Kids with musical talent
    B. Handsome kids
    C. Kids from Dublin
    D. Kids who could make him laugh

(c) What was the name of the earlier film that John Carney directed?

    A. *The Commitments*
    B. *Once*
    C. *Frozen*
    D. *The American Dream*

(d) What is the difference between the band in *The Commitments* and the band in *Sing Street*?

    A. The band in *The Commitments* was American
    B. The band in *Sing Street* wrote their own songs
    C. The band in *The Commitments* wrote their own songs
    D. The band in *The Commitments* admired U2

Question 2   **10 marks**

How were the members of U2 helpful to John Carney when he was writing and directing the film *Sing Street*?

_____

_____

_____

_____

_____

_____

_____

_____

_____

_____

Question 3   **20 marks**

You have been given the job of directing a film or play that you studied.

(a)   Name the film **or** play that you studied: _____

(b)   Name an important character from your chosen film or play:_____

(c)   Describe a key moment in the film or play where your named character plays a significant
            role.

┌───┐
│   │
│   Optional rough work   │
│   │
│   │
│   │
│   │
│   │
│   │
│   │
└───┘

_____

_____

_____

_____

_____

_____

_____

_____

_____

_____

_____

_____

(d) Did you like or dislike what your named character did in the key moment you have described? Give a reason for your answer.

_____

_____

_____

_____

_____

_____

_____

_____

_____

(e) Give one piece of advice to an actor playing the part of your named character, about how he or she should act during this key moment. Why do you think this piece of advice would help the actor to play the part well?

_____

_____

_____

_____

_____

_____

_____

_____

_____

_____

_____

Additional writing space. Label all work clearly with the question number and part.

Read the following extract from the graphic novel, *American Born Chinese* by Gene Luen Yang.

94

Question 4   **10 marks**

Describe what happens in the first four frames of this story (page 9).

Optional rough work

_____

_____

_____

_____

_____

_____

_____

_____

_____

_____

_____

_____

_____

_____

_____

_____

Question 5   **5 marks**

Look at frames 8 and 9. Which one of the following two words do you think best describes Wei-Chen's reaction when Jin tells him about Amelia?

- Mean

  or

- Funny

Give a reason for your answer.

_____

_____

_____

_____

_____

_____

_____

_____

_____

_____

Question 6   **10 marks**

Look at the next frame in the story which shows Jin lying in bed the night he has discovered that his friend Wei-Chen now has a girlfriend. Fill in the thought box with what you think Jin may have been thinking.

Optional rough work

Question 7   **5 marks**

This is an extract from a graphic novel. Graphic novels use a mixture of pictures and text to tell a story. Do you like this way of telling a story? Give a reason for your answer.

_____

_____

_____

_____

_____

_____

_____

_____

_____

_____

Question 8   **30 marks**

Choose a novel or a short story you have studied.

(a)   Name of novel or short story: _____

(b)   Author: _____

(c)   Describe a moment in the story that you particularly enjoyed reading.

Optional rough work

_____
_____
_____
_____
_____
_____
_____
_____
_____
_____
_____

(d)   Why did you enjoy your chosen moment? Give reasons for your answer.

_____
_____
_____
_____
_____
_____
_____
_____
_____
_____
_____
_____

(e) Do you think the author is a good writer? Give reasons for your answer.

_____

_____

_____

_____

_____

_____

_____

_____

_____

_____

_____

Additional writing space. Label all work clearly with the question number and part.

_____

_____

_____

_____

_____

_____

_____

_____

_____

_____

_____

_____

2017

Read the following two newspaper reports, one from a broadsheet paper and one from a tabloid paper.

REPORT A

GREEN ARMY GOES BARMY AFTER WIN

The Lille Stadium was rocked off its feet last night as Ireland produced one of the great football nights in the country's history.

A Green Army of 15,000 fans were sent into raptures as a brilliant Robbie Brady goal was enough to slay the Italians and send the fans into Euro 2016 heaven.

Brady's header six minutes from time was met with absolute bedlam in the stands as Irish fans danced and cheered the team on to victory.

"This is one of the best nights of my life," fan John Connolly said proudly.

Irish fans now face a trek to Lyon to take on hosts France on Sunday.

The Irish fans were in fine voice throughout the match. However, the fans vented most of their anger at the referee, who denied two penalties near the stroke of half time.

REPORT B

REMAINING IN EUROPE

Republic of Ireland 1 Italy 0

The Republic of Ireland will play tournament hosts France in the next round of Euro 2016 after another famous 1-0 victory over Italy, this time on an emotional night in Lille.

Twenty-two years after Ray Houghton proved the hero against Italy in the World Cup game in Giant's Stadium, New Jersey, it was the turn of Robbie Brady to write his name into sporting history last night.

But Brady was only one of many Irish heroes in the game, including manager Martin O'Neill, who made sweeping changes to the team that lost to Belgium and was rewarded with a performance of great courage and skill. The victory leads on to Lyon where the Republic will play France next Sunday, kicking off at 2pm.

From the start last night, the Republic responded to assistant manager Roy Keane's call for physicality, threatening to turn the game into a football version of the Battle of the Somme.

Question 9   **5 marks**

The broadsheet and tabloid newspaper reports above are about the same event. State in one sentence what that event was.

_____

_____

Question 10   **10 marks**

State whether the following is true or false, by writing either T (true) or F (false) in the box provided.

Report A is from a tabloid newspaper.   ☐

Explain your choice.

_____

_____

_____

_____

Report B is from a broadsheet newspaper.

Explain your choice.

_____

_____

_____

Question 11   **10 marks**

Write an opening paragraph for a newspaper report about **one** of the topics below. You should include an appropriate headline.

- Musician wins major award
- Fan meets his or her hero
- Sportsperson achieves huge success

+---+
| Optional rough work |
| |
| |
| |
| |
| |
| |
+---+

Headline:

_____

_____

Paragraph for report:

_____

_____

_____

_____

_____

_____

_____

_____

_____

_____

Question 12   **10 marks**

You have had an unpleasant experience at a big public event that you were really looking forward to, such as a concert or sports event. Write an email in which you describe your experience to either:

A friend
or
The organisers of the event.

Your email should be written in a suitable style.

Optional rough work

Additional writing space. Label all work clearly with the question number and part.

Read the following poem carefully and answer the questions.

Sporty People

I took her for my kind of person
And it was something of a shock
When my new friend revealed
That, once upon a time,
She was a Junior County Tennis Champion.

How could that happen?
How could I accidentally
Make friends with a tennis champion?
How could a tennis champion

Make friends with me?

She wasn't stupid. She read books.
She had never been mean to me
For being bad at games.
I decided to forgive
Her unfortunate past.

Sporty people can be OK -
Of course they can.
Later on, I met poets
Who played football. It's still hard
To get my head around that.

Wendy Cope

Question 13   **5 marks**
What was the poet shocked to discover about her friend?

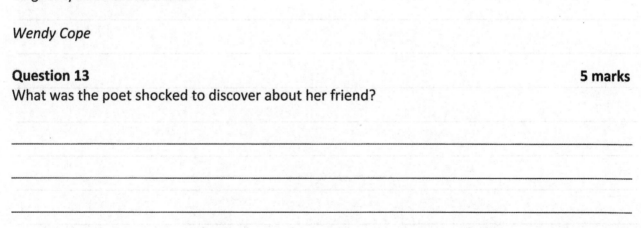

_____

_____

_____

_____

Question 14   **5 marks**

Do you think the poet likes sporty people? Give a reason for your answer.

_____

_____

_____

_____

Question 15   **15 marks**

The theme of this paper is _Following Your Passions_. Choose a poem you have studied that you would recommend to others. You may not use the poem printed on this paper in your answers.

(a)   Title of poem: _____

(b)   Name of poet: _____

+---+
| |
| Optional rough work |
| |
| |
| |
| |
| |
| |
| |
+---+

(c)   Why would you recommend your chosen poem to others?

_____

_____

_____

_____

_____

_____

_____

(d) You are making a short film, based on your chosen poem, to put online. What would you show in this film to help others to enjoy the poem?

_____

_____

_____

_____

_____

_____

_____

_____

_____

_____

_____

_____

_____

_____

Question 16   **10 marks**

You are the host of a TV chat show, interviewing a person who has followed their own passion in life.

(a) Name the person: _____ (The person can be real or imaginary.)

(b) What is your chosen person passionate about? _____

(c) Part **(c)** of this question is on page 26.

Part **(c)** of this question is on page 26.

Optional rough work

(c) Write a short text of the interview that you imagine takes place between you and your chosen person in which you discuss what they are passionate about. Use the following line as your opening:

Host: Good evening, my guest on tonight's show is a person I admire greatly, please welcome …

_____

_____

_____

_____

_____

_____

_____

_____

_____

_____

_____

_____

_____

_____

_____

_____

_____

_____

_____

_____

_____

Question number	Write the question numbers in the left-hand margin
	....

Acknowledgements

Images

Image on page 87: *Sing Street*. John Carney. The Weinstein Company, 2016
Images on pages 93, 94, 95, 98: Gene Luen Yang: *American Born Chinese*
Image on page 102: skysports.com
Image on page 107: freepik.com (15 February 2017)

Texts

Interview with John Carney from *www.theverge.com*
Gene Luen Yang: *American Born Chinese*
Cope, Wendy: *Sporty People*
The Irish Times, The Irish Daily Star

Material may have been adapted, for the purpose of assessment, without the authors' prior consent.

Junior Cycle 2017
Final Examination

English
Ordinary Level

Wednesday 7 June
Morning 9:30 to 11:30

Coimisiún na Scrúduithe Stáit
State Examinations Commission

Junior Cycle 20XX
Final Examination Sample 1

English

Ordinary Level

Day Date June – Morning 9:30 to 11:30

180 marks

Examination number

Centre Stamp

The theme of this examination paper is
Young People and the World

Instructions

There are **three** sections in this examination paper.

Section A	Reading Comprehension	70 marks	6 Questions
Section B	Writing for a Variety of Purposes	50 marks	2 Questions
Section C	Responding Imaginatively	60 marks	6 Questions

Answer all fourteen questions.

The questions do not all carry equal marks. The number of marks for each question is stated at the top of the question.

You should spend about forty minutes on Section A and about thirty-five minutes each on Section B and Section C.

When answering on studied material, you must use texts prescribed for examination in 201X.

Write your answers in the spaces provided in this booklet. You may lose marks if you do not do so. Space is provided for extra work. Label any extra work clearly with the question number and part.

Section A   Reading Comprehension – Young People and Adventure

Study the two cinema posters for the film *Song of the Sea*. Complete the tasks that follow.

Poster 1

Poster 2

Question 1   **10 marks**

Based on what you can see in both of the posters, write the letter corresponding to the correct answer in the box.

(a)   The film *Song of the Sea* opens in cinemas on,

    A.   The ninth of December

    B.   The nineteenth of November

    C.   December the nineteenth

    D.   December the ninth

(b)   As a rating, one of the reviews awards the film,

    A.   Four stars

    B.   Thumbs up

    C.   Five stars

    D.   An Oscar

(c)   The director of *Song of the Sea* also directed a film called,

    A.   The Academy Award

    B.   Dazzling

    C.   The Secret of Kells

    D.   A Beautiful Film

(d)   When one of the reviews says that the film is 'Spellbinding' it means that,

    A.   The film is about wizards and magicians

    B.   You will leave the cinema feeling dizzy

    C.   The film will hold your interest completely

    D.   The film is confusing

Question 2   **5 marks**

Based on what you can see in the two posters, who do you think would enjoy this film? Explain your answer.

_____

_____

_____

_____

Study the still pictures taken from the film *Song of the Sea*. Still pictures are pictures taken from a film where the action is frozen. Complete the tasks that follow.

1.

2.

3.

4.

Question 3   **10 marks**

Based on what you can see in the still pictures on page 33, write a paragraph that starts with one of the following prompts.

The pictures made me think that the film is **humorous** because ...

or

The pictures made me think that the film is **imaginative** because ...

Fill in the blank and continue with your choice.

The pictures made me think that the film is _____ because ...

_____

_____

_____

_____

_____

_____

_____

_____

_____

_____

_____

_____

Question 4   **5 marks**

The film *Song of the Sea* was praised for the way that it used colour and light. Do you agree?
Give a reason for your answer based on what you can see in the still pictures on page 33.

_____

_____

_____

_____

_____

_____

_____

_____

_____

Question 5   **10 marks**

Based on the still pictures (on page 33) and the posters (on page 31), would you like to see the film *Song of the Sea*? Give reasons for your answer.

Optional Rough Work

_____

_____

_____

_____

_____

_____

_____

_____

_____

_____

_____

_____

Question 6

Read the following letter, written by the young actor David Rawle. David performed the voice of one of the characters in *Song of the Sea*. Answer the questions that follow.

I think it was somewhere around July of 2012 when I first heard about Song of the Sea, and I was interested straight away. I remember bringing out the bins when my Mam came outside and said that she had a phone call from Paul Young from an animation studio based in Kilkenny called Cartoon Saloon, asking if I would voice a part in their new film. Cartoon Saloon had done the animation for a show I was in called Moone Boy.

I had never done any voice acting before and I was fascinated by the whole thing. I went for the audition in Kilkenny and I remember feeling nervous. I went inside a room and read extracts from the script. I got word that I had gotten the part a few weeks later.

On our first day of recording I met Fionnuala Flanagan and I remember my Dad shaking Brendan Gleeson's hand. We had brilliant fun in those few days and I was sad to say goodbye.

The Premiere in London was the first time any of us had seen the full movie. Then everything changed on the Thursday the 14th January. We knew the movies nominated for the Oscars would be announced. Mam looked at her phone and told us "Song of the Sea has been nominated for an Oscar!" I was absolutely shocked and delighted.

I met up with Tomm and Paul on "The Late Late Show" for an interview and they casually asked me if I'd like to go to Hollywood, Los Angeles, California in a few weeks; I'm still surprised I didn't faint! I had never been to America before and I was excited to visit all the sites.

Paul whipped out two tickets to the Oscars, one with my name on it. There was a mad rush that day to rent a tuxedo. Of course, I didn't sleep a wink that night. The next morning we all suited up and I went for my first ride in a limo. We didn't win but people aren't lying when they say the real win is the nomination.

I met some of the nicest and funniest people while making Song of the Sea. I'm so, so proud to have been part of this incredible movie.

Write one sentence to answer each of the following questions:

What was David doing when he first heard about *Song of the Sea*?

_____

_____

What was the name of the animation studio that made *Song of the Sea*?

_____

_____

Where was the Premiere of the film held?

_____

_____

What award was the film nominated for?

_____

_____

How did the makers of *Song of the Sea* surprise David on the 'Late Late Show'?

_____

_____

How did David travel to the award ceremony?

_____

_____

The film did not win the award on the night. Based on what you have read, how would you describe David's feelings afterwards?

_____

_____

_____

What do you think David learned from his experience of being involved with the film?

_____

_____

_____

Additional Writing Space. Label all work clearly with the question number and part.

Section B   Writing For a Variety of Purposes

Question 7   **24 marks**

Using the questions provided, write an article for your school magazine in which you describe an exciting new experience you had.

What was the new experience?

_____

_____

_____

_____

How did you first hear about it and what were your feelings at the time?

_____

_____

_____

_____

What was the most exciting part of the experience and why was it the most exciting part?

_____

_____

_____

_____

What did you think and how did you feel when the experience was over?

_____

_____

_____

_____

What title would you give your article?

_____

_____

_____

Question 8   **26 marks**

Choose a film that you have studied.

Title of Film:

_____

Name of Film Director:

_____

Imagine you are a film reviewer on a television programme for young people. Write the script for a review of your chosen film using the following prompts.

Introduce the film.

_____

_____

_____

_____

Explain what the film was about.

_____

_____

_____

_____

_____

_____

Talk about the most interesting character in the film.

_____

_____

_____

_____

_____

_____

_____

_____

What did you like or dislike about the film?

_____

_____

_____

_____

_____

_____

_____

_____

_____

How would you rate the film?

_____

_____

_____

_____

_____

_____

Additional Writing Space. Label all work clearly with the question number and part.

Read 'The Rebel' by D.J. Enright and then answer the questions that follow.

The Rebel

When everybody has short hair,
The rebel lets his hair grow long.

When everybody has long hair,
The rebel cuts his hair short.

When everybody talks during the lesson,
The rebel doesn't say a word.

When nobody talks during the lesson,
The rebel creates a disturbance.

When everybody wears a uniform,
The rebel dresses in fantastic clothes.

When everybody wears fantastic clothes,
The rebel dresses soberly*.

When everybody says, yes please,
The rebel says, no thank you.

When everybody says, No thank you,
The rebel says, yes please.

It is very good that we have rebels,
You may not find it very good to be one.

*Plainly

Question 9   **10 marks**

From your understanding of the poem, write the letter corresponding to the correct answer in the box.

(a)   When all of the other students are wearing their hair short, the rebel decides to ...

    A.   Copy them

    B.   Grow his hair long

    C.   Skip school

    D.   Pay extra attention in class

(b)   When the rest of the class is being quiet, the rebel ...

    A.   Does his homework

    B.   Skips class

    C.   Asks the teacher for help

    D.   Makes noise and misbehaves

(c)   When all of the other students wear bright clothes, the rebel ...

    A.   Copies them

    B.   Wears plain clothes

    C.   Wears his school uniform

    D.   Wears a hat

(d)   When all of the other students are talking in class, the rebel ...

    A.   Is silent

    B.   Gets upset

    C.   Takes part in the discussion

    D.   Laughs at them

(e)   The last verse of the poem means that ...

    A.   It is important that there are people in the world who do things differently even though it may not be easy for those people

    or

    B.   It is easy to be a rebel in this world; it is harder to behave properly

Question 10   **10 marks**

Write a sentence using each of the following words correctly. In your sentence you should try to show what each of the words mean. You may not use a line from 'The Rebel'.

(a) Lesson

_____

_____

_____

(b) Disturbance

_____

_____

_____

(c) Uniform

_____

_____

_____

(d) Fantastic

_____

_____

_____

(e) Rebel

_____

_____

_____

Question 11   **10 marks**

Would you like to be the rebel described in this poem? Give a reason for your answer.
Use lines from the poem to help support your points.

+---+
| Optional Rough Work |
| |
| |
| |
| |
+---+

_____

_____

_____

_____

_____

_____

_____

_____

Question 12   **10 marks**

If you had the chance to give the rebel one piece of advice, what would it be? Explain your answer.

_____

_____

_____

_____

_____

_____

_____

_____

_____

Question 13   **10 marks**

A broken window is discovered in one of the classrooms of the school. The principal is sure that the rebel is responsible. The rebel is called to the principal's office.

Write the text of the conversation you think might take place between them. Show clearly who is talking at each point of the conversation.

Use **Principal** and **Rebel** to show who is talking.

Optional Rough Work

Question 14   **10 marks**

Choose a poem that you have studied. Write about your chosen poem using **one** of the following prompts as a guide for your writing:
You may use quotes from the poem to help explain your point of view.

- The poem made me laugh because ...

or

- The poem made me angry because ...

or

- The poem made me think because ...

Name of Poem: _____

Name of Poet: _____

The poem made me _____ because ...

```
┌─────────────────────────────────────────────────────────────────────┐
│                        Optional Rough Work                            │
│                                                                       │
│                                                                       │
│                                                                       │
│                                                                       │
│                                                                       │
│                                                                       │
│                                                                       │
└─────────────────────────────────────────────────────────────────────┘
```

_____

_____

_____

_____

_____

_____

_____

_____

_____

Additional Writing Space. Label all work clearly with the question number and part.

Additional Writing Space. Label all work clearly with the question number and part.

Acknowledgments

Images

Images on pages 115, 120: cartoonsaloon.ie
Image on page 124: bbc.co.uk
Images on page 125: googleimages
Image on page 127: theguardian.co.uk
Image on page 131: wallpaperswide.com

Texts

"Song of the Sea, Special Education Supplement." The Sunday Independent, 7 July 2015
Enright, D.L., *The Rebel*, https://neoenglish.wordpress.com. (Accessed 10 September 2015)

Texts may have been adapted, for the purpose of assessment, without the authors' prior consent

Junior Cycle 20XX
Final Examination Sample 1

English
Ordinary Level

Wednesday X June
Morning 9:30 to 11:30

Junior Cycle 20XX
Final Examination Sample A

English

Ordinary Level

Day Date June – Morning 9:30 to 11:30

180 marks

Examination number

The theme of this examination paper is
Mysteries

Instructions

There are **three** sections in this examination paper.

Section A	Reading to Understand	35 marks	5 questions
Section B	Reflecting on Reading	80 marks	5 questions
Section C	Imagining and Creating	65 marks	5 questions

Answer all 15 questions.

The questions do not all carry equal marks. The number of marks for each question is stated at the top of the question.

You should spend about 35 minutes on Section A
You should spend about 45 minutes on Section B
You should spend about 35 minutes on Section C

When answering on studied material, you must use texts prescribed for examination in 20XX.

Write your answers in the spaces provided in this booklet. You may lose marks if you do not do so. You are not required to use all the space provided. You should read each question in full before beginning your response.

Extra pages are provided if needed. Label any extra work clearly with the question number and part.

You may only use blue or black pen when writing your answers. Do not use pencil.

The examination booklet will be scanned and your work will be presented to an examiner on screen. Anything that you write outside of the answer areas may not be seen by the examiner.

Suggested time for Section A: 35 minutes

Read this extract from Roddy Doyle's novel, *A Greyhound of a Girl*, and answer the questions which follow.

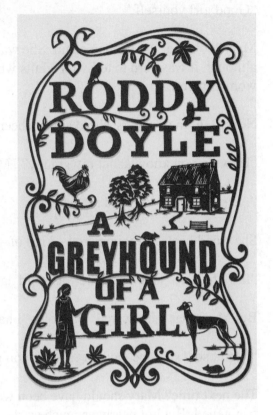

Mary is on her way home from school when she meets a mysterious woman.

"That's a wet day."

Someone had just spoken to Mary. But she couldn't see anyone. She was alone on the street just outside her house.

Then she saw the woman. She must have been behind one of the trees, Mary thought.

The woman was old. But actually, she wasn't.

Mary knew what it was, why the woman seemed old. She was old-fashioned. She was wearing a dress that looked like it came from an old film, one of those films her mother always cried at. She looked like a woman who milked cows and threw hay with a pitchfork. She was even wearing big boots with fat laces.

A bird above them must have flown away quickly, because the leaves shook and dropped loads of water on their heads. May laughed – she felt the raindrops – but the woman didn't seem to notice. Nothing about her was wet.

"It's a wet day, alright," she said. "Did you get loads of homework, did you?"

"The usual," said Mary.

"What's the usual when it's at home?"

Mary laughed again. The woman sounded like her grandmother. But then that made her sad, and angry again. She was going to cry – she thought she was.

"What's wrong with you?" said the woman.

"My granny's not well," said Mary.

"Sure, I know," said the woman.

"Well why did you ask then?" said Mary.

"God, you're a rip, alright."

"What does that mean?"

"You're a cheeky young lady," said the woman.

"Everyone says that," said Mary. "That I'm cheeky. But I'm not. I'm just honest."

"Good girl yourself."

Mary looked at the woman again. She wasn't old at all. She looked younger than Mary's mother, although it was hard to tell with adults what age they were. Mary was sure she'd never seen this woman before.

Never talk to strangers, she'd always been told. But she did – now.

"How do you know about my granny?" Mary asked the woman.

"Ah sure, I just do," said the woman.

She stood back and shimmered – kind of – as if she was stepping behind a sheet of clear plastic.

"It's life," she said – and she was solid again, and smiling.

But Mary was a bit scared, and cold. "I have to go," she said.

"Right, so," said the woman … "Off you go, so. I'll see you next time."

The next time? Mary should have been worried, even frightened. She *was* worried and a bit frightened. But not nearly as much as she thought she should have been.

This text has been adapted from the original for the purpose of assessment, without the author's prior consent.

Question 1   (5 marks)

From your reading of this extract, what do you think is Mary's reaction to the mysterious woman? Give a reason for your answer.

Optional Rough Work

_____

_____

_____

_____

_____

Question 2 (5 marks)

Which **one** of the following words best describes how you feel when you read this extract from the novel?

- Curious
- Clever

Explain your answer.

_____

_____

_____

_____

_____

_____

Question 3 (5 marks)

Based on your reading of this extract from the novel, what do you think is the mysterious woman's attitude to Mary? Explain your answer.

_____

_____

_____

_____

_____

_____

Question 4 (10 marks)

Did you enjoy this extract? Explain **two** reasons why you did or did not in your response.

Optional Rough Work

_____

_____

_____

_____

_____

_____

_____

_____

_____

_____

Question 5 (10 marks)

Your friend is going to write a mystery story for her Junior Cycle English Collection of Texts. Give two pieces of advice you would offer your friend on how to write this story. Explain why you think this advice would be useful.

Optional Rough Work

_____

_____

_____

_____

_____

_____

_____

_____

Suggested time for Section B: 45 minutes

Read this ballad by Walter de la Mare and then answer the questions which follow.

Tom's Angel

No one was in the fields
But me and Polly Flint,
When, like a giant across the grass,
The flaming angel went.

It was budding time in May,
And green as green could be,
And all in his height he went along
Past Polly Flint and me.

We'd been playing in the woods,
And Polly up, and ran
And hid her face, and said,
"Tom! Tom! The Man! The Man!"

And I up-turned; and there,
Like flames across the sky,
With wings all bristling, came
The Angel striding by.

And a chaffinch overhead
Kept whistling in the tree
While the angel, blue as fire, came on
Past Polly Flint and me.

And I saw his hair, and all
The ruffling of his hem,
As over the clovers his bare feet
Trod without stirring them.

Polly – she cried; and, oh!
We ran, until the lane
Turned by the miller's roaring wheel,
And we were safe again.

Question 6   **(5 marks)**

Based on your reading of the poem, which **one** of the following statements is false? Place a tick (✓) in one box only.

Tom and Polly ran down the lane to the miller's wheel.   ❑

Polly was not frightened by the angel.   ❑

The chaffinch kept singing in the tree when the angel passed by.   ❑

Question 7 (10 marks)

Give **two** examples of similes in the poem.

Simile 1: _____

Simile 2: _____

Question 8 (10 marks)

Ballads were written to be memorised. What makes "Tom's Angel" easy to learn by heart?

Optional Rough Work

_____

_____

_____

_____

_____

_____

_____

_____

_____

_____

_____

_____

144

Question 9 (15 marks)

Write a description of a mysterious creature using **three** similes or comparisons. (The creature can be based on one from a text or can be an original creation from your imagination.)

Optional Rough Work

_____

_____

_____

_____

_____

_____

_____

_____

_____

_____

_____

Question 10 (40 marks)

Read all parts of the question before starting your answer.

Optional Rough Work

(a) Choose a novel or film you have studied where something mysterious or unusual happens.

Title of novel or film: _____

(b) Describe the mysterious or unusual event or element.

_____

_____

_____

_____

_____

_____

_____

_____

_____

_____

(c) Name the central character in the novel or film you chose in (a) above.

Name of central character: _____

(d) What, if anything, was the effect of the unusual or mysterious event/happening on the central character?

_____

_____

_____

_____

_____

_____

_____

_____

_____

_____

(e) How did the novel or film end?

_____

_____

_____

_____

_____

_____

_____

(f) Was the ending a satisfactory one? Explain your answer.

_____

_____

_____

_____

_____

_____

_____

Suggested time for Section C: 35 minutes

These images and captions present a series of places and moods. Study them carefully and answer the questions which follow.

IMAGE A: A Convenient Perch

IMAGE B: And Still Falls The Rain

IMAGE C: And Miles To Go Before I Sleep

IMAGE D: The Mysterious Woods

IMAGE E: The Faces In The Crowd

IMAGE F: They Sit In Silence

EDCO EXAM PAPERS

Assessment Task and Revision Notes

NEW JUNIOR CYCLE
ENGLISH

HIGHER & ORDINARY LEVEL

Reference Only

THE EDUCATIONAL COMPANY OF IRELAND

First published 2022

The Educational Company of Ireland
Ballymount Road
Walkinstown
Dublin 12

www.edco.ie

A member of the Smurfit Kappa Group plc

Welcome to the new Junior Cycle for English

Reference Only

The Edco examination papers will help you prepare for your final Junior Cycle English examination. They will also give you practice in becoming a better reader, a better writer and a better thinker.

The English Assessment Tasks will help you prepare for your classroom-based Assessment Task. They will also give you practice in reflecting on your writing across a range of genres.

The quick revision checklists in this booklet will help you think about your work and the features which give it quality and, in the case of writing, make it rewarding to read.

Contents

Assessment Task

Assessment Task: Introduction

The Assessment Task is completed in your classroom in an examination booklet.

Knowledge and Skills
The Assessment Task relates to the knowledge and skills you developed in preparing your texts for The Collection of Texts Classroom-Based Assessment, and your reflection on that process.

Marking
- The Assessment Task is sent to the State Examinations Commission. It is marked as part of your Final Examination.
- The combination of the Assessment Task and the Final Examination generates your grade.
- Up to 10% of your grade comes from the Assessment Task and 90% comes from the Final Examination.

Learning Outcomes
- The Collection of Texts Classroom-Based Assessment covers a wide range of Learning Outcomes.
- The most important of these is W4 – your ability to write in a range of forms, using appropriate vocabulary, tone and a variety of styles to achieve your purpose.

Writing the Assessment
- You are permitted to have the two texts you submitted to your teacher as well as previous drafts and any reflections you completed when writing these texts, during the written part of the Assessment Task.
- These can be referred to, examined or quoted from.

Two Class Periods
- The task is completed over two class periods.
- In the first period you read (watch/listen to) and then discuss a piece of stimulus material for approximately 15 minutes.
- The focus of the discussion is your experience of the process of creating texts.
- For the remaining 25 minutes, you are given time to reflect and prepare for the written task. You will have an opportunity to read the questions in the booklet and think about how you might respond to the prompts.
- In your next English class, you will complete the booklet.
- You will have approximately 35 minutes to complete this task with 5 minutes to label and submit your answer booklet.

Junior Cycle Assessment Task

Based on Assessment Task of January 2020

English

20 Marks

Instructions

Answer all three questions.

Write your answers in the spaces provided in this booklet. Do not enclose or attach any other work, as this will not be marked.

Visit www.e-xamit.ie to access assessment task sample answers

Question 1   **(2 marks)**

Give the titles of two texts, from your collection of texts, that you consider to be your best writing and identify the genre of each text.

First text: _____

Genre: _____

Second text: _____

Genre: _____

Select an extract (for example, a paragraph, passage, or verse) from one text identified above. Copy the extract into the space provided below. The extract should not exceed 100 words approximately.

_____

_____

_____

_____

_____

_____

_____

_____

_____

_____

_____

_____

_____

_____

_____

_____

Question 2 (8 marks)

Write a response to either **(a) or (b)**. Place a tick in the box next to your choice.

(a) Explain how two features of the extract you have chosen are typical of its genre. ☐

Or

(b) Identify a change that you made in the course of writing this text that you think improved it and explain how it improved the text. ☐

_____

_____

_____

_____

_____

_____

_____

_____

_____

_____

_____

_____

_____

_____

_____

_____

_____

_____

_____

_____

_____

_____

_____

Question 3   **(10 marks)**

Thinking about the process of writing/compiling your Collection of Texts, write a short paragraph in response to each of **two** of the following **prompts** into the spaces provided in the booklet:

Prompts

       a)   How I came up with ideas for one of my texts
       b)   Something I have discovered about writing from creating my Collection of Texts
       c)   How I worked with classmates to develop my writing skills
       d)   How I considered my audience when writing one of my texts

In your responses, you are encouraged to refer to specific texts from your collection.

Prompt ( ) _____

Response

_____

_____

_____

_____

_____

_____

_____

_____

Prompt ( ) _____

Response

_____

_____

_____

_____

_____

_____

Junior Cycle Assessment Task
Based on Assessment Task of November 2018
English

20 Marks

Instructions

Answer all three questions.

Write your answers in the spaces provided in this booklet. Do not enclose or attach any other work, as this will not be marked.

Visit www.e-xamit.ie to access assessment task sample answers

Question 1   **(2 marks)**

Give the titles of two texts, from your collection of texts, that you consider to be your best writing and identify the genre of each text.

First text: _____

Genre: _____

Second text: _____

Genre: _____

Select an extract (for example, a paragraph, passage, or verse) from one text identified above. Copy the extract into the space provided below. The extract should not exceed 100 words approximately.

_____

_____

_____

_____

_____

_____

_____

_____

_____

_____

_____

_____

_____

_____

_____

_____

Question 2 (8 marks)

Write a response to either **(a) or (b)**. Place a tick in the box next to your choice.

(a) Explain how two features of the extract you have chosen are typical of its genre.

Or

(b) Identify a change that you made in the course of writing this text that you think improved it and explain how it improved the text.

_____

_____

_____

_____

_____

_____

_____

_____

_____

_____

_____

_____

_____

_____

_____

_____

_____

_____

_____

_____

_____

_____

Question 3   **(10 marks)**

Thinking about the process of writing/compiling your Collection of Texts, write a short paragraph in response to each of **two** of the following **prompts** into the spaces provided in the booklet.

Prompts

   a)   How a writer inspired my writing
   b)   How I edit my writing to improve it
   c)   How feedback helps me as a writer
   d)   The text from my collection I like best and why

In your responses, you are encouraged to refer to specific texts from your collection.

Prompt ( ) _____

Response

_____

_____

_____

_____

_____

_____

_____

Prompt ( ) _____

Response

_____

_____

_____

_____

_____

_____

_____

Junior Cycle Assessment Task
Based on Assessment Task of April 2018
English

20 Marks

Instructions

Answer all three questions.

Write your answers in the spaces provided in this booklet. Do not enclose or attach any other work, as this will not be marked.

Visit www.e-xamit.ie to access assessment task sample answers

Question 1   **(2 marks)**

Give the titles of two texts, from your collection of texts, that you consider to be your best writing and identify the genre of each text.

First text: _____

Genre: _____

Second text: _____

Genre: _____

Select an extract (for example, a paragraph, passage, or verse) from one text identified above. Copy the extract into the space provided below. The extract should not exceed 100 words approximately.

_____

_____

_____

_____

_____

_____

_____

_____

_____

_____

_____

_____

_____

_____

_____

_____

Question 2 (8 marks)

Write a response to either **(a) or (b)**. Place a tick in the box next to your choice.

(a) Explain how two features of the extract you have chosen are typical of its genre. ☐

Or

(b) Identify a change that you made in the course of writing this text that you think improved it and explain how it improved the text. ☐

_____

_____

_____

_____

_____

_____

_____

_____

_____

_____

_____

_____

_____

_____

_____

_____

_____

_____

_____

_____

_____

_____

_____

Question 3   **(10 marks)**

Choose two prompts from the prescribed list. (See below). Write a response to each of your chosen prompts in the spaces provided. You are encouraged to refer to specific texts from your collection.

Prompts

     a)   How I came up with ideas for one of my texts

     b)   How I worked with classmates to develop my writing skills

     c)   A genre I would like to write in again and why?

     d)   What a reader might enjoy about one of the texts in my collection

In your responses, you are encouraged to refer to specific texts from your collection.

Prompt ( ) _____

Response

_____

_____

_____

_____

_____

_____

_____

Prompt ( ) _____

Response

_____

_____

_____

_____

_____

_____

_____

Revision Notes

Advice on Reading

Try to read the texts on the examination papers in an active way. Active reading means reading a text with a determination to understand, interpret and assess or evaluate it for yourself. The following questions will help you get the most out of your reading.

Active Reading

❑ Did I ask relevant questions before, during and after reading the text?

❑ Did I ask relevant questions about the text, the writer and my own response?

❑ Did I make notes, write comments and highlight as I read?

❑ Did I identify and underline key words and phrases?

❑ Did I read between the lines?

❑ Did I identify the tone of the piece of writing?

❑ Did I make predictions, as I read, based on clues in the text?

❑ Did I make connections with other texts as I read?

❑ Did I compare one text to another?

❑ Did I relate what I read to my own life and to the world?

❑ Did I use context, re-reading and questions to help me understand new or difficult passages of text?

❑ Did I use my imagination to visualise the images in the text?

❑ Did I interpret the meaning of the text and identify the main themes?

❑ Did I evaluate the text?

Advice on Writing

No matter what you are writing, neat handwriting, correct spelling, careful punctuation and the use of paragraphs will enhance the experience of your reader. The following checklist will help you remember key points about good punctuation.

Punctuation

❑ Did I start each sentence with a capital letter and end it with one of the following: a full stop (.), a question mark (?) or an exclamation mark (!)?

❑ Did I use commas to separate the words in a list?

❑ Did I use commas to mark off one part of a sentence from another?

❑ Did I use a comma to separate direct speech from the rest of the sentence?

❑ Did I use an apostrophe to show ownership?

❑ Did I use an apostrophe to show where letters have been left out of a word?

❑ Did I use speech marks (inverted commas) around spoken words?

❑ Did I use a semi colon (;) to separate the equal parts in a sentence?

❑ Did I leave a space between the end of one paragraph and the beginning of another?

Reference Only

Spelling

Make sure that you know how to spell the most common words used in English. This list will help you.

nouns		verbs		adjectives	
animal	number	asked	said	able	last
babies	part	called	saw	bad	little
case	people	came	say	beautiful	long
child	person	feel	see	big	many
children	place	felt	started	different	new
clothes	point	found	stopped	early	next
company	problem	get	take	few	old
day	school	give	telling	first	other
eye	something	going	think	frightened	own
fact	thing	have	thought	good	public
friend	time	knew	took	great	right
government	way	know	tried	high	same
hand	week	leave	try	important	small
life	woman	look	use	interesting	young
man	work	make	wanted	large	
money	world	running	want		
morning	year				
mother					

Stories

Writing stories is one of the most enjoyable activities in English. This checklist will help you include the key elements in your story.

Character

❑ Did I create my story around an interesting character?

❑ Did I convey both the positive and negative sides of my character's personality?

❑ Did I describe my character's situation?

❑ Did I capture the character's voice in the story?

Plot

❑ Did I introduce the other key characters?

❑ Did I keep the plot simple?

❑ Did I include conflict?

❑ Did my central character change as a result of the conflict?

Writing

❑ Did I choose my words and phrases with real care?

❑ Did I create clear pictures in my readers' minds?

❑ Did I describe one or more memorable incidents?

❑ Did I describe the thoughts and feelings of my central character?

❑ Did I use dialogue in the most dramatic parts of the story?

Story Shape

❑ Did I catch the reader's attention from the opening of the story?

❑ Did I include a revelation that causes some upset to the central character?

❑ Was there tension or suspense in the story?

❑ Did I include a moment of conflict?

❑ Did the central character have to make an important decision?

❑ Did the story have a suitable ending?

Diaries and Letters

Often you are asked to write in the voice of a character, especially in the form of diary entries. This checklist will help you write in a convincing way.

- ❑ Did I provide convincing details?
- ❑ Did I describe situations and people clearly and specifically?
- ❑ Did I capture the emotions of the diarist?
- ❑ Did the diary entries help the reader under-stand the thoughts and feelings of the diarist?
- ❑ Did the diary entries help the reader see events from the point-of-view of the diarist?
- ❑ Did the diary entries contain details and descriptions that showed I used my imagination?
- ❑ Did the language of the entries catch the voice of the diarist?

Letters

You may be asked to write a letter either in your own voice or in the voice of a character. These two checklists will help with both formal and personal letters.

Formal Letter

- ❑ Did I give a clear structure to the letter?
- ❑ Did I include my address?
- ❑ Did I date the letter?
- ❑ Did I include a formal greeting?
- ❑ Did my introduction state the purpose of the letter?
- ❑ Was the letter written in an appropriate, formal tone?
- ❑ Did I include a formal closing statement?
- ❑ Did I include a full signature?

Personal Letter

- ❑ Was it clear from the beginning that I was writing to someone I know?
- ❑ Did I write in a natural way?
- ❑ Was my reason for writing the letter clear?
- ❑ Did I include interesting details?
- ❑ Did I use a conversational tone?
- ❑ Did I use a friendly greeting and closing?
- ❑ Did I sign the letter?

Persuasive Writing

Persuasive writing is all about changing minds or getting others to agree with your point-of-view. The most popular form of persuasive writing is the speech.

Awareness of Audience

❏ Was I aware of my audience?

❏ Did I tailor my speech to suit the interests of my audience?

Quality and Organisation of Content

❏ Did I catch the interest of the audience from the beginning of my speech?

❏ Did I state my position clearly?

❏ Did I choose my words carefully?

❏ Did I use interesting or startling examples to support my argument?

❏ Were my ideas well presented?

❏ Did I link my ideas together?

❏ Did I summarise my argument?

❏ Was my point-of-view clear?

❏ Did I finish on a strong note?

Different Styles

❏ Did I write in a confident manner?

❏ Did I write with conviction?

❏ Did I use emotive language to sway my audience?

❏ Did I create clear pictures in the minds of my audience?

❏ Did I use personal pronouns to connect to my audience?

❏ Did I use repetition for emphasis?

❏ Did I use lists to build up momentum?

❏ Did I make good use of rhetorical questions?

Discursive Writing

Discursive writing sets out to present a fair and balanced discussion of a topic. The most popular form of discursive writing is the essay. It is always a good idea to use linking words and phrases to establish a clear relationship between different parts of your essay. Here are some useful examples.

Similar line of thought	Contrasting ideas	Definite statements	Further examples	Conclusion/ summary
firstly secondly next furthermore likewise moreover similarly also in addition	on the other hand however yet on the contrary conversely although but	without doubt without question questionably undeniably absolutely	for instance for example so that accordingly such as since unless	therefore consequently as a result hence in conclusion to summarise thus accordingly so

The following phrases are useful for introducing a new point.

For	Against
In addition Moreover Furthermore It is the view of many people that ... Some believe/think/feel that ... While some may believe, others are of the view that ... Although some people would have us believe	However, there are arguments against this point-of-view On the other hand, it can be said that ... Nevertheless, there is another side to the argument Despite the fact that there is some truth in this ... It can also be argued that another point to be taken into consideration is ....

The following questions will help you review your essay.

- ❏ Did I state the topic in the first paragraph?
- ❏ Did I make reasonable arguments?
- ❏ Did I explain my thinking?
- ❏ Was my essay balanced? Did I give both sides of the argument?
- ❏ Did I use connectives to link paragraphs?
- ❏ Did I use quotes or references to support my arguments?
- ❏ Did I make my opinion clear in the closing paragraph?
- ❏ Did I say whether it was easy or difficult to reach a conclusion and explain why this was so?

Report Writing

Sometimes in an examination you might be asked to write a report, either in your own voice or in the voice of a character. Reports should be written in a clear, factual manner. This checklist will help you think about the elements of a well-written report.

- ❑ Was my report clearly labelled and titled?
- ❑ Was it laid out in paragraphs?
- ❑ Did I write the report in a clear way, using simple, factual language?
- ❑ Was the tone of my report impersonal?
- ❑ Did I check for spelling and grammatical errors?
- ❑ Did I present the information in a logical order?
- ❑ Did I make sure that each paragraph had a clear structure?
- ❑ Did I use connecting words and phrases to link paragraphs?
- ❑ Did the ideas flow from one paragraph to the next?
- ❑ Was my first paragraph clear and focused?
- ❑ Did my concluding paragraph give a summary of the main points of the report?
- ❑ Did I include any recommendations?

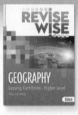

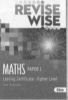
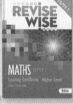
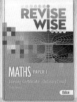

Question 11   **(5 marks)**

In your view, which image and caption sparks your imagination? Explain your answer.

_____

_____

_____

_____

_____

_____

_____

Question 12   **(5 marks)**

Choose a second image. Choose five words to describe it. Choose your words carefully.

I choose Image _____

_____

_____

_____

_____

_____

_____

_____

_____

Question 13   **(30 marks)**

Read all parts of the question carefully before starting your answer.

(a) You have been asked to choose a poem that you think is successful in capturing a mood or describing a place in a vivid way.

Title of poem: _____

Name of poet: _____

(b) Give a short summary of your chosen poem.

_____

_____

_____

_____

_____

_____

_____

(c) Why, do you think, is your chosen poem successful in capturing a mood or describing a place? Explain your answer.

_____

_____

_____

_____

_____

_____

_____

_____

_____

_____

_____

(d) What kind of person do you imagine the poet who wrote your chosen poem to be? Give reasons for your answer.

_____

_____

_____

_____

_____

_____

_____

_____

_____

_____

Question 14 (5 marks)

Read the following sentence:

The black crow perching on the green **post suddenly rose into** the air.

Complete the table using each of the words in bold from the sentence above. The first example is completed for you. Use each word only **once.**

Definite Article	The
Verb	
Preposition	
Adjective	
Noun	
Adverb	

Question 15 (20 marks)

Write the opening paragraph of a personal essay called 'A Special Place'. Your aim is to make the opening so interesting that readers will want to learn more.

A Special Place

Optional Rough Work

_____

_____

_____

Junior Cycle 20XX
Final Examination Sample B

English

Ordinary Level

Day Date June – Morning 9:30 to 11:30

180 marks

20XX. XXX

Examination number

The theme of this examination paper is
Food

Instructions

There are **four** sections in this examination paper.

Section A	Communicating and Responding	60 marks	5 questions
Section B	Writing for a Variety of Purposes	35 marks	3 questions
Section C	Choosing the Words and Tone to Use	50 marks	4 questions
Section D	Appreciating Visual Genres	35 marks	4 questions

Answer all **sixteen** questions.

The questions do not all carry equal marks. The number of marks for each question is stated at the top of the question.

You should spend about 40 minutes on Section A. You should spend about 20 minutes on Section B. You should spend about 35 minutes on Section C. You should spend about 20 minutes on Section D.

When answering on studied material, you must use texts prescribed for examination in 20XX.ß

Write your answers in the spaces provided in this booklet. You may lose marks if you do not do so. Space is provided for extra work. Label any extra work clearly with the question number and part.

You may only use blue or black pen when writing your answers. Do not use pencil.

The examination booklet will be scanned and your work will be presented to an examiner on screen. Anything that you write outside of the answer areas may not be seen by the examiner.

Read this extract from Bruce Chatwin's novel _On the Black Hill_ and answer the questions which follow. Benjamin and Lewis are twins. The passage describes their first memory.

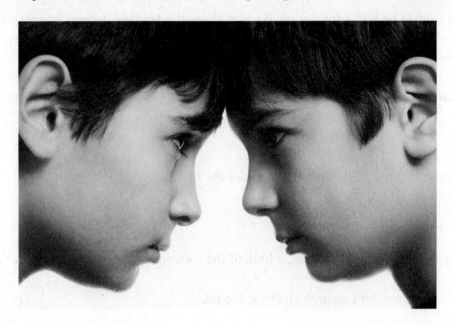

The twins' first memory – a shared memory which both remembered equally well – was of the day they were stung by a wasp.

They were perched on high-chairs at the tea-table. It must have been teatime because the sun was streaming in from the west, bouncing off the table-cloth and making them blink. It must have been late in the year, perhaps as late as October, when wasps are drowsy. Outside the window, a magpie hung from the sky, and bunches of red rowanberries thrashed in the gale. Inside, the slabs of bread-and-butter glistened the colour of primroses. Mary was spooning egg-yolk into Lewis's mouth and Benjamin, in a fit of jealousy, was waving his hands to attract attention when his left hand hit the wasp, and was stung.

Mary rummaged in the medicine cupboard for cotton-wool and ammonia, dabbed the hand and, as it swelled and turned scarlet, said soothingly, 'Be brave, little man! Be brave!'

But Benjamin did not cry. He simply pursed his mouth and turned his sad grey eyes on his brother. For it was Lewis, not he, who was whimpering with pain, and stroking his own left hand as if it were a wounded bird. He went on snivelling till bedtime. Only when they were locked in each other's arms did the twins doze off – and from then on, they associated eggs with wasps and mistrusted anything yellow.

This was the first time Lewis demonstrated his power to draw the pain from his brother, and take it on himself.

He was the stronger twin, and the firstborn.

To show he was the firstborn, Dr. Bulmer nicked a cross on his wrist; and even in the cradle he was the stronger. He was unafraid of the dark and of strangers. He loved to rough-and-tumble with the sheepdogs. One day, when nobody was about, he squeezed through the door of the beast-house, where Mary found him, several hours later, gabbling away to the bull.

By contrast, Benjamin was a terrible coward who sucked his thumb, screamed if separated from his brother, and was always having nightmares – of getting caught in a chaffcutter, or trampled by carthorses. Yet whenever he really did get hurt – if he fell in the nettles or walloped his shin – it was Lewis who cried instead.

They slept in a truckle bed, in a low-beamed room along the landing, where, in another early memory, they woke one morning to find that the ceiling was an unusual shade of grey. Peering out, they saw the snow on the larches, and the snowflakes spiralling down.

When Mary came in to dress them, they were curled, head to toe, in a heap at the bottom of the bed.

'Don't be silly,' she said. 'It's only snow.'

'No, mama,' came two muffled voices from under the blankets. 'God's spitting.'

Question 1 (10 marks)

(a) Indicate, by marking the correct box, which of the following statements is true or false.

1 The twins were perched on high chairs at the table. ☐ True ☐ False

2 It was teatime and the sun was set. ☐ True ☐ False

3 Outside the window, a crow hung from the sky. ☐ True ☐ False

4 It was late August and the wasps were drowsy. ☐ True ☐ False

5 The bread and butter glistened the colour of tulips. ☐ True ☐ False

(b) What was Benjamin doing when he was stung?

_____

_____

_____

_____

_____

Question 2 (10 marks)

On the evidence of stanza three, what kind of mother was Mary? Explain your answer.

_____

_____

_____

_____

On the Black Hill by Bruce Chatwin. Published by Jonathan Cape. Reprinted by permission of The Random House Group.

_____

Question 3   **(10 marks)**

Based on the text, identify the major differences between the twins.

_____

Question 4   **(15 marks)**

"This was the first time Lewis demonstrated his power to draw the pain from his brother, and take it on himself."

(a) Do you find this an interesting idea? Explain your answer.

_____

(b) The writer gives the reader this piece of information at the beginning of his story. Suggest why he did this.

_____

_____

_____

_____

_____

_____

(c) Would you like to read more about the twins and their life? Give reasons for your answer.

Optional Rough Work

_____

_____

_____

_____

_____

_____

_____

_____

_____

Question 5   **(15 marks)**

Imagine a situation in their later life when Lewis drew pain from his brother and took it on himself. Describe what happened.

+---+
| Optional Rough Work |
| |
| |
| |
| |
| |
| |
| |
+---+

_____

_____

_____

_____

_____

_____

_____

_____

EDCO SAMPLE B

Question 6   **(5 marks)**

Use three adjectives to describe the appearance of a bee.

Adjective 1 _____

Adjective 2 _____

Adjective 3 _____

Question 7   **(15 marks)**

Write an account, real or imagined, of an occasion when you were stung by a bee or a wasp.
Use the following questions to shape your answer.

Where were you and what were you doing before you were stung?

_____

_____

_____

_____

_____

What caused the bee or the wasp to sting you?

_____

_____

_____

_____

_____

What did it feel like immediately after you received the sting?

_____

_____

_____

_____

How did you react?

_____

_____

_____

_____

What was the reaction of those around you?

_____

_____

_____

_____

How did your story end?

_____

_____

_____

_____

How do you feel about bees and wasps now?

_____

_____

_____

_____

Question 8 (15 marks)

Write a mouth-watering account of eating your favourite food. Pay attention to the sound of the words you choose. Paint a picture of fun and sunshine with your words.

_____

_____

_____

_____

_____

_____

_____

_____

_____

_____

_____

_____

_____

Read this poem by William Carlos Williams and then answer the questions which follow.

This Is Just To Say

I have eaten
the plums
that were in
the icebox

and which
you were probably
saving
for breakfast

Forgive me
they were delicious
so sweet
and so cold

Question 9   **(10 marks)**

The poem only has 28 words. Does this add to or take away from your enjoyment?
Explain your answer.

Optional Rough Work

Question 10 (10 marks)

Choose three words from the poem which you think express what it is like to eat a soft fruit.

Word 1 _____

I chose this word because _____

_____

_____

_____

Word 2 _____

I chose this word because _____

_____

_____

_____

Word 3 _____

I chose this word because _____

_____

_____

_____

Question 11 (10 marks)

How would you feel if you were the 'you' of the poem and found this poem on the door
of your fridge?

    – I would feel offended. I wouldn't find it funny.
    – I would feel amused and laugh.
    – I would feel delighted that someone had written me a lovely poem.
    – I would feel angry that someone had eaten my breakfast.
    – I would feel cheated.

Explain your choice.

Optional Rough Work

164

_____

_____

_____

_____

_____

_____

_____

_____

_____

_____

_____

_____

_____

_____

_____

Question 12   **(20 marks)**

Choose a poem that you have studied which made a big impression on you.

Give the name of the poem: _____

Give the name of the poet: _____

(a) Explain why the poem made an impression on you.

_____

_____

_____

_____

_____

_____

_____

(b) Give your view of the use of language in the poem.

_____

_____

_____

_____

_____

_____

_____

(c) Give your view of the imagery in the poem.

_____

_____

_____

_____

_____

_____

_____

Study this infographic and then answer the questions which follow.

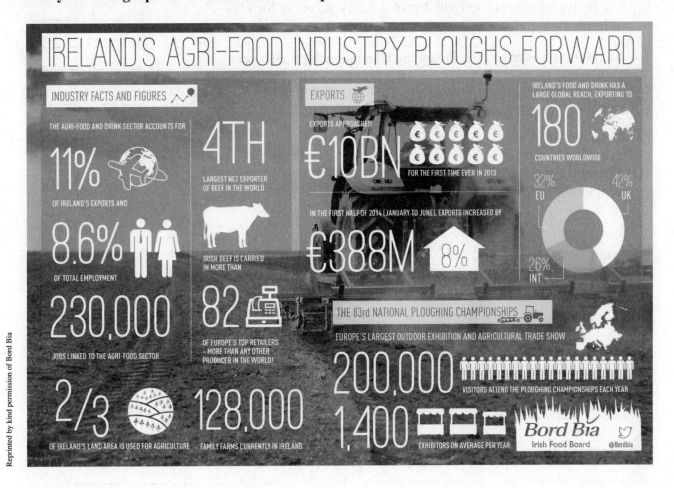

IRELAND'S AGRI-FOOD INDUSTRY PLOUGHS FORWARD

INDUSTRY FACTS AND FIGURES

THE AGRI-FOOD AND DRINK SECTOR ACCOUNTS FOR

11%
OF IRELAND'S EXPORTS AND

8.6%
OF TOTAL EMPLOYMENT

230,000
JOBS LINKED TO THE AGRI-FOOD SECTOR

2/3
OF IRELAND'S LAND AREA IS USED FOR AGRICULTURE

4TH
LARGEST NET EXPORTER OF BEEF IN THE WORLD

IRISH BEEF IS CARRIED IN MORE THAN

82
OF EUROPE'S TOP RETAILERS – MORE THAN ANY OTHER PRODUCER IN THE WORLD!

128,000
FAMILY FARMS CURRENTLY IN IRELAND

EXPORTS

EXPORTS APPROACHED

€10BN
FOR THE FIRST TIME EVER IN 2013

IN THE FIRST HALF OF 2014 (JANUARY TO JUNE), EXPORTS INCREASED BY

€388M 8%

THE 83rd NATIONAL PLOUGHING CHAMPIONSHIPS
EUROPE'S LARGEST OUTDOOR EXHIBITION AND AGRICULTURAL TRADE SHOW

200,000
VISITORS ATTEND THE PLOUGHING CHAMPIONSHIPS EACH YEAR

1,400
EXHIBITORS ON AVERAGE PER YEAR

IRELAND'S FOOD AND DRINK HAS A LARGE GLOBAL REACH, EXPORTING TO

180
COUNTRIES WORLDWIDE

32% EU   42% UK
26% INT

Bord Bia
Irish Food Board   @Bordbia

Question 13   (10 marks)

What is the message from the banner headline on this infographic? Choose from A, B, C below.

   A – The Irish agricultural food and drinks industry is making good progress.

   B – The Irish agricultural food and drinks industry is falling behind its international
        competitors.

   C – The Irish agricultural food and drinks industry is under-developed.

I choose _____ because: _____

_____

_____

Question 14   **(10 marks)**

Tick true or false in response to the following statements.   True   False

(a) The Irish agricultural food and drinks industry accounts for 11%
    of Ireland's exports.   ☐   ☐

(b) 100,000 visitors attend the Ploughing Championships each year. ☐   ☐

(c) The Irish agricultural food and drinks industry exports to over
    180 countries worldwide.   ☐   ☐

(d) One-third of Ireland's land area is used for agriculture.   ☐   ☐

(e) The Irish agricultural food and drinks industry accounts for over
    20% of total employment in Ireland.   ☐   ☐

Question 15   **(5 marks)**

In your view, what is the most surprising statistic in the Infograph?

_____

_____

_____

_____

_____

_____

_____

_____

_____

_____

_____

_____

_____

_____

Question 16   **(10 marks)**

Write a catchy slogan that the organisers of the annual Ploughing Championships might use to attract 10–15-year-olds to the event.

_____

_____

_____

_____

_____

Additional Writing Space. Label all work clearly with the question number and part.

_____

_____

_____

_____

_____

_____

_____

Junior Cycle 20XX
Final Examination Sample C

English

Ordinary Level

Day Date June – Morning 9:30 to 11:30

180 marks

20XX. XXX

Examination number

The theme of this examination paper is
Zoos

Instructions

There are **three** sections in this examination paper.

Section A	Appreciating Language and Imagery	100 marks	5 questions
Section B	Responding to Studied Texts	55 marks	4 questions
Section C	Reading Comprehension	25 marks	2 questions

Answer all **eleven** questions.

The questions do not all carry equal marks. The number of marks for each question is stated at the top of the question.

You should spend about 60 minutes on Section A.
You should spend about 35 minutes on Section B.
You should spend about 15 minutes on Section C.

When answering on studied material, you must use texts prescribed for examination in 20XX.

Write your answers in the spaces provided in this booklet. You may lose marks if you do not do so. Space is provided for extra work. Label any extra work clearly with the question number and part.

You may only use blue or black pen when writing your answers. Do not use pencil.

The examination booklet will be scanned and your work will be presented to an examiner on screen. Anything that you write outside of the answer areas may not be seen by the examiner.

Read this poem by Leonard Clarke and answer the questions which follow.

Lion

Poor prisoner in a cage,
I understand your rage
And why you loudly roar
Walking that stony floor

Your forest eyes are sad
As wearily you pad
A few yards up and down,
A king without a crown

Up and down all day
A wild beast for display,
Or lying in the heat
With sawdust, smells and meat,

Remembering how you chased
Your jungle prey and raced,
Leaping upon their backs
Along the grassy tracks.

But you are here instead,
Better, perhaps, be dead
Than locked in this dark den;
Forgive us, lion, then,
Who did not ever choose
Our circuses and zoos.

Question 1   **(20 marks)**

(a) Who is the poet talking to in the poem?

_____

_____

_____

(b) Which of the following words best describes the tone of the poem?

– sad
– angry
– bitter

I think the word _____ best describes the tone of the poem, because

_____

_____

_____

_____

(c) Would you describe the rhythm of the poem as fast or slow? Explain your answer.

_____

_____

_____

_____

(d) The poem has rhymes. Do the rhymes make the poem seem happy or sad? Explain your answer.

_____

_____

_____

_____

Question 2 (10 marks)

What pictures are brought to your mind by the phrase 'forest eyes'?

_____

_____

_____

_____

_____

_____

_____

_____

Question 3 (30 marks)

(a) In four sentences suggest the difference between the lion's life in the zoo and his life in the wild.

> Optional Rough Work

1 _____
_____
_____

2 _____
_____
_____

3 _____
_____
_____

4 _____
_____
_____

(b) What two words or phrases sum up the lion's life in the zoo? Explain your answer

I chose _____

because _____
_____

and I chose _____

because _____
_____

(c) What two words or phrases sum up the lion's life in the wild?

I chose _____

because _____

_____

and I chose _____

because _____

_____

Question 4 (20 marks)

In the final stanza, the poet asks forgiveness of the lion. Do you think we should ask forgiveness of the animals kept in captivity in our zoos?
Write the text of short speech to be delivered to your class on this question, using the guidelines provided.

> Optional Rough Work

Opening – setting out where you stand on the question.

_____

_____

_____

_____

_____

_____

Supporting points

_____

_____

_____

_____

_____

_____

EDCO SAMPLE C

Summing up

_____

_____

_____

_____

_____

Question 5 (20 marks)

Choose a poem about animals that you have read and enjoyed.

Title of the poem: _____

Name of the poet: _____

(a) In two sentences say what it was about the poem that you really liked.

_____

_____

_____

_____

_____

(b) Pick one image from the poem that you liked and say why you liked it.

_____

_____

_____

_____

_____

(c) Give one example of the poet's choice of words that you liked and say why you liked it.

_____

_____

_____

_____

_____

(d) In two sentences say what you thought was the theme of the poem.

_____

_____

_____

_____

Additional Writing Space. Label all work clearly with the question number and part.

_____

_____

_____

_____

_____

_____

_____

_____

_____

_____

_____

_____

_____

_____

_____

_____

_____

_____

_____

Give the title and author or director of a novel or film you studied which dealt with the theme of freedom and answer the questions which follow.

Title of text: _____

Name of writer/director: _____

Question 6   (10 marks)

Describe the life of the central character. Was it, for example, a happy life?

Optional Rough Work

_____

_____

_____

_____

_____

_____

_____

_____

_____

_____

Question 7   (25 marks)

(a) Did you identify with the central character? Explain your answer.

Optional Rough Work

_____

_____

_____

_____

_____

(b) Do you think the central character was a hero? Give reasons for your answer.

_____

_____

_____

_____

(c) For you, what qualities make a hero?

_____

_____

_____

_____

_____

Question 8 (**10 marks**)

What was the most interesting idea in the novel? Explain your choice.

```
                        Optional Rough Work



```

_____

_____

_____

_____

_____

_____

_____

_____

_____

Question 9   **(10 marks)**

If you were to sum up the message of the text in one paragraph, what would it be?

```
                        Optional Rough Work




```

_____

_____

_____

_____

_____

_____

_____

_____

_____

180

Read the extract from a radio interview with Laurel Braitman about her book on animal madness and then answer the questions which follow. The interviewer was Don Gonyea.

GONYEA: You don't just write about dogs. You write about gorillas who've been neglected and then who have trouble connecting to other gorillas once they grow up. How do you think understanding this kind of behavior helps us maybe even understand humans?

BRAITMAN: It helps a lot. The gorillas at Boston's Franklin Park Zoo, for example, have a human psychiatrist. He treated Gigi, an elderly female gorilla at the Franklin Park Zoo, for what he believed is a panic disorder, PTSD, and a mood disorder.

GONYEA: In the book, you talk a lot about how we can understand animal behavior by looking at it through the lens of human behavior. What about – what about the opposite? How does this research help us to understand humans?

BRAITMAN: Well, first of all, what I learned was that almost everything that we know about the unhinged human mind, we learned from watching other animals. So everything from a concept of emotional resilience (…) to a lot of what we've learned about the kinds of things that infants need for healthy development, we learned from watching monkeys. A monkey who has been denied affection just won't become a healthy adult. So those are just some examples.

But really, almost everything that cheers up your dog is also going to cheer you up. So things like exercise and if you're a social animal, getting to know another social animal who may be a little bit more emotionally healthy than you is really helpful. And that doesn't even have to be the same species as you. So, you know, goats can cheer up dogs and tortoises can cheer up hippos. It's not just the stuff of Internet forwards and memes is what I discovered.

GONYEA: I wonder, how has writing this book changed the way you interact with animals, if it has?

BRAITMAN: Well, first of all, I'm a really weird zoo-goer. You can be like every other person there, which is, first, you know, we always pull out our hand and we do, like, a jaunty open-palmed human hello, as if they're going to wave back to us. And then we pull out the camera phone. And then we nudge the person next to us. And we say, look, they're just like us. And then we keep walking on.

But actually, if you want a slightly more meaningful encounter, you should try to be a slightly more entertaining person. And if you do something like – you take off your shoes, for example. A lot of apes want to see your toes. A lot of animals will be interested if you hold up a young infant to the glass.

At the Bronx Zoo, according to the guides, the gorillas' favorite day of the year is Halloween, when adults and kids come to the zoo dressed in costume. All the gorillas come up to the glass and they're curious because for one day out of the year we're interesting. That's just one tiny example. I have so many in the book of all of the ways that this work surprised me into more complex views of the creatures around me…

Question 10 (10 marks)

Write a sentence using each of the following words in a correct way to show its meaning. You may not use any sentences from Laurel Braitman's text.

(a) neglected

_____

_____

_____

(b) unhinged

_____

_____

_____

(c) resilience

_____

_____

_____

(d) species

_____

_____

_____

(e) complex

_____

_____

_____

_____

Question 11   **(15 marks)**

Here are some reactions to this interview with Laurel Braitman. Which one is closest to your own?

1   "What Laurel Braitman says about animals applies to humans, as well."

2   "I love the idea of being an entertaining person at the zoo. I'm going to try to be one next time I visit a zoo."

3   "I don't think we should treat animals as if they are humans. They're not."

4   "The message from this interview is that we should look more carefully at the world around us."

_____

_____

_____

_____

_____

_____

_____

_____

_____

_____

_____

Additional Writing Space. Label all work clearly with the question number and part.

Junior Cycle 20XX
Final Examination Sample D

English

Ordinary Level

Day Date June – Morning 9:30 to 11:30

180 marks

20XX. XXX

Examination number

The theme of this examination paper is
Mothers and Fathers

Instructions

There are **three** sections in this examination paper.

Section A	Reading to Understand	75 marks	6 questions
Section B	Engaging the Reader	55 marks	3 questions
Section C	Responding Imaginatively to Studied Texts	50 marks	2 questions

Answer all **eleven** questions.

The questions do not all carry equal marks. The number of marks for each question is stated at the top of the question.

You should spend about 45 minutes on Section A.
You should spend about 35 minutes on Section B.
You should spend about 30 minutes on Section C.

When answering on studied material, you must use texts prescribed for examination in 20XX.

Write your answers in the spaces provided in this booklet. You may lose marks if you do not do so. Space is provided for extra work. Label any extra work clearly with the question number and part.

You may only use blue or black pen when writing your answers. Do not use pencil.

The examination booklet will be scanned and your work will be presented to an examiner on screen. Anything that you write outside of the answer areas may not be seen by the examiner.

Read this extract from Jackie Kay's autobiography and answer the questions which follow.

Mummy why aren't you the same colour as me?
1969

I am seven years old. My mum, my brother and I have just watched a cowboy and Indian film. I'm sad because the Indians have lost again, and I wanted them to win. It suddenly occurs to me that the Indians are the same colour as me and my mum is not the same colour as me. I say to my mum, Mummy why aren't you the same colour as me? My mum says, Because you are adopted. I say, What does adopted mean?

My brother scoffs; Don't you know what adoption means? I can't believe you don't know what adoption means. He's eating a giant-size bowl of cornflakes. He eats cornflakes for nearly every meal. No, I don't know. I'm nearly in tears. I've heard the word before but I don't really understand it. My mum says, It means I'm not really your mummy. What do you mean, you're not really my mummy? I say. I am crying for real now because I love my mum so much and I want her to be my real mummy and I'm worried she means she is not real and that something is going to happen to her, that she is going to disappear or dissolve. She says, Your real mother couldn't keep you so she gave you to me so that I could be your mummy. Yes, and that means you're not really my sister, my brother laughs. Ha ha. Do you get it? Are you making this up? I ask my mummy. Is this one of your stories? She's so good, my mummy, at telling stories. No, it isn't, she says. She's in tears herself too. It's upset her. Your real daddy comes from Nigeria in Africa and your mummy came from the Highlands. What, I say, so my daddy isn't my real daddy either? No, my mum says. I'm distraught. I can't stop crying. I love them both so much the idea that people I have never met are my real parents and not them is horrible. How long have you known about this? I ask my brother, furious with him for some reason because he's laughing and finds the whole thing very funny. I've known for ages. I can't remember not knowing, he says. So it's good, isn't it? You're not my real sister. Ha! Ha! My mum goes out of the room and comes back and wipes her face on a tea towel. She says, But your dad and I love you more than all the tea in China, more than all the waves in the ocean and will love you till all the seas run dry. And you are special. You were chosen. And everyone needs cuddles to survive. Everyone needs cuddles, so they do. Come here and let your mummy give you a big cuddle.

Question 1 **(20 marks)**

The young Jackie asks her mum questions. For each of her questions below, write in your own words the answers she receives.

(a) Why aren't you the same colour as me?

Answer: _____

_____

_____

_____

_____

(b) What does adopted mean?

Answer: _____

_____

_____

_____

_____

(c) What do you mean, you're not really my mummy?

Answer: _____

_____

_____

_____

_____

(d) Are you making this up?

Answer: _____

_____

_____

_____

_____

Question 2 (5 marks)

Based on this extract, what kind of woman is Jackie's mum?

_____

_____

_____

_____

_____

Question 3 (10 marks)

Select **two** phrases or lines from the passage which show how the young Jackie feels about the mum and dad she lives with.

My first choice is: _____

_____

I chose this because: _____

_____

_____

_____

My second choice is: _____

_____

I chose this because: _____

_____

_____

_____

Question 4 (10 marks)

Which one of these words best describes what Jackie feels when she learns that she is adopted?

- confused
- afraid
- curious

I choose _____ because: _____

_____

_____

_____

_____

_____

_____

_____

_____

_____

_____

Question 5   **(10 marks)**

How does the writer capture a seven-year-old child's way of speaking and thinking?

Optional Rough Work

_____

_____

_____

_____

_____

_____

_____

_____

EDCO SAMPLE D

191

Question 6 (20 marks)

Imagine you are Jackie's mum. You have just put a tearful Jackie to bed. She is still upset that you told her you are not her 'real' mum. You decide to write her a letter to tell her how much she is loved and that nothing will change. Write the letter. You can use some of the mum's words from the text in your letter.

Optional Rough Work

Read this extract from Des Bishop's autobiographical book, *My Dad Was Nearly James Bond*, and answer the questions which follow.

1. When I was a kid I believed every one of my dad's stories. As far as I was concerned he was pretty famous when he was younger. I did not know much else about his life other than his career as an actor and a model. He has been in the British Army and had lived in Midleton, County Cork, during World War II. Sometimes he would be watching TV and would recognise someone he knew from the past. One I always remember was Robert Shaw from *Jaws*. *Jaws* was a big movie and the fact that my dad knew someone from it was pretty cool.

2. All my friends loved my dad. They loved his accent and he would always tell them ghost stories. He was great at doing Dracula stories. I can still picture a large group of us, sitting in the living room one early evening while my dad was telling one of his stories, and how mesmerised we were by it. He was a great performer for my friends. It's cool when you are young and the girls that you are beginning to take notice of tell you that your dad is cool.

3. When we were kids, there wasn't much to dislike about my dad, but he didn't really have much authority in the house. My mother was the boss. To us, our dad was just cool and fun. He never gave us a hard time about school or homework, he just encouraged us to do well in sports. Up until I hit puberty, most of the time I just saw my dad as a really cool guy. I was too young to be aware that he was not the authority figure, he was just the guy I wanted to impress. 'Dad, watch me dive off the diving board.' 'Dad, count how long I can stay under water.' He was our hero.

4. But it all changed when I became a teenager. I developed a desire to challenge my dad's authority. I went from thinking my parents were the coolest people on the planet to thinking they were the dumbest people on earth. I think American writer, Mark Twain, said it best when he said, "When I was a boy of fourteen, my father was so ignorant I could hardly stand to have the old man around. But when I got to be twenty-one, I was astounded by how much he'd learned in seven years." I had entered my period of rebellion and my brothers would enter that period at two year intervals behind me. We expressed it by making fun of my father all the time. When my dad went from being the only person we wanted to impress, he became the butt of our jokes and our attempts to impress each other. We were like fanatical fans who turn on their idols with a vengeance. We had outgrown his style. He was not cool anymore.

Question 7   (20 marks)

Find an example of each of the following in the text, which help to make Des Bishops's writing engaging:

Optional Rough Work

Humour

_____

I chose this example because: _____

_____

_____

_____

An Interesting Fact

I chose this example because: _____

_____

_____

_____

_____

Honesty

I chose this example because: _____

_____

_____

_____

_____

Question 8 (10 marks)

Would reading this extract from Des Bishop's book inspire you to write about your own family?

_____

_____

```
┌─────────────────────────────────────────────┐
│              Optional Rough Work              │
│                                               │
│                                               │
│                                               │
│                                               │
│                                               │
└─────────────────────────────────────────────┘
```

Explain your answer.

_____

_____

_____

_____

_____

_____

_____

_____

Question 9   **(25 marks)**

Choose a text you have studied for your course which you found really engaging.

Title of text: _____

Name of author: _____

(a) You are sharing your opinion with the rest of your class. Introduce the text and briefly describe what it is about.

_____

_____

_____

_____

_____

_____

_____

_____

_____

(b) Explain **two** things which you found really engaging about the text – these can relate to the story, the characters or the way the story was told.

┌───┐
│   Optional Rough Work   │
│   │
│   │
│   │
│   │
│   │
└───┘

_____

_____

_____

_____

_____

_____

_____

_____

_____

_____

(c) Describe how you felt when you finished reading this text.

_____

_____

_____

_____

_____

_____

_____

_____

_____

(d) Rate the text for your fellow students.

_____

_____

_____

_____

Section C   Responding Imaginatively to Studied Texts

Question 10   **(20 marks)**

Choose your favourite character from a novel, film or play you studied for your course.

Name of the character: _____

Title of the text: _____

(a) Give three reasons why this is your favourite character.

> **Optional Rough Work**

Reason 1: _____

_____

_____

_____

_____

Reason 2: _____

_____

_____

_____

_____

Reason 3: _____

_____

_____

_____

_____

(b) Describe your favourite moment in the text involving the character named above.

> **Optional Rough Work**

Question 11 (30 marks)

Imagine you are your favourite character. You are writing your autobiography. Write about an incident from your childhood involving one or both of your parents. Make your writing as engaging as possible. You can use the opening line below as a prompt.

> **Optional Rough Work**

I was seven years old and the world was a happy place ....

Additional Writing Space. Label all work clearly with the question number and part.

Junior Cycle 20XX
Final Examination Sample E

English

Ordinary Level

Day Date June – Morning 9:30 to 11:30

180 marks

20XX. XXX

Examination number

The theme of this examination paper is
Sharing the Planet

Instructions

There are **three** sections in this examination paper.

Section A	Reading to Appreciate	85 marks	4 questions
Section B	Responding Imaginatively to Texts	30 marks	1 question
Section C	Reading to Understand a Persuasive Text	65 marks	5 questions

Answer all **ten** questions.

The questions do not all carry equal marks. The number of marks for each question is stated at the top of the question.

You should spend about 50 minutes on Section A.
You should spend about 20 minutes on Section B.
You should spend about 40 minutes on Section C.

When answering on studied material, you must use texts prescribed for examination in 20XX.

Write your answers in the spaces provided in this booklet. You may lose marks if you do not do so. Space is provided for extra work. Label any extra work clearly with the question number and part.

You may only use blue or black pen when writing your answers. Do not use pencil.

The examination booklet will be scanned and your work will be presented to an examiner on screen. Anything that you write outside of the answer areas may not be seen by the examiner.

Read this extract from Andy Mulligan's novel *Trash*. The novel tells the story of two boys, Raphael and Gardo, who live by sorting through the rubbish in the dumpsite and selling anything that can be recycled.

So where do we start?

My unlucky-lucky day, the day the world turned upside down? That was a Thursday. Me and Gardo were up by one of the crane-belts. These things are huge, on twelve big wheels that go up and down the hills. They take in the trash and push it up so high you can hardly see it, then tip it out again. They handle the new stuff and you're not supposed to work there because it's dangerous. You're working under the trash as it's raining down, and the guards try to get you away.

Gardo's fourteen, same as me. He's thin as a whip, with long arms. He was born seven hours ahead of me, onto the same sheet, so people say. He's not my brother but he might as well be, because he always knows what I'm thinking, feeling – even what I'm about to say. The fact that he's older means he pushes me around now and then, tells me what to do, and most of the time I let him. People say he's too serious, a boy without a smile, and he says, 'So show me something to smile at.' He can be mean, it's true – but then again he's taken more beatings than me so maybe he's grown up faster. One thing I know is I'd want him on my side, always.

We were working together, and the bags were coming down – some of them already torn, some of them not – and that's when I found a 'special'. A special is a bag of trash, unsplit, from a rich area, and you always keep your eyes wide for one of them. I can remember even now what we got. A cigarette cartoon, with a cigarette inside – that's a bonus. A pen, probably no good, and pens are easy to come by, and some dry papers I could stick straight in my sack – then trash and trash, like old food and a broken mirror or something, and then falling into my hand … I know I said you don't find interesting things, but, OK – once in your life …

It fell into my hand: a small leather bag, zipped up tight and covered in coffee grinds. Unzipping it, I found a wallet. Next to that, a folded-up map – and inside the map – a key. Gardo came right over, and we squatted there together, up on the hill. My fingers were trembling, because the wallet was fat. There were eleven hundred pesos inside and that – let me tell you – is good money. A chicken costs one-eighty … one hour in the video hall, twenty-five.

I sat there laughing and saying a prayer. Gardo was punching me and I don't mind telling you, we almost danced.

Question 1   **(35 marks)**

(a) *Good writers create interesting characters.* Identify three things that make Gardo an interesting character.

Optional Rough Work

1 _____

_____

_____

_____

2 _____

_____

_____

_____

3 _____

_____

_____

_____

(b) *Good writers set their stories in interesting places.* What makes the setting of this story interesting?

Optional Rough Work

_____

_____

_____

_____

_____

_____

_____

_____

_____

_____

(c) *Good writers know how to keep their readers wanting to find out more.* What are the questions left unanswered in this extract from the novel?

```
Optional Rough Work




```

_____

_____

_____

_____

_____

_____

_____

_____

_____

Question 2 **(10 marks)**

Explain why this could be described as a key scene in the story.

Optional Rough Work

_____

_____

_____

_____

_____

_____

_____

_____

_____

_____

Question 3 **(10 marks)**

Raphael is the narrator of the story. Suggest two elements of his character that you learned from this passage.

1 _____

_____

_____

_____

2 _____

_____

_____

_____

Question 4   **(30 marks)**

Name a novel, short story or film you studied in which two characters share everything.

Name of text: _____

Name of author/director: _____

(a) Describe the world in which the characters live.

Optional Rough Work

_____

_____

_____

_____

_____

_____

_____

_____

_____

_____

(b) Did the characters have a good relationship?

Optional Rough Work

_____

_____

_____

_____

_____

_____

_____

_____

_____

_____

_____

(c) Was one character more of a leader than the other? Explain your answer.

Optional Rough Work

_____

_____

_____

_____

_____

_____

_____

_____

Question 5   **(30 marks)**

Taking your inspiration from *Trash* by Andy Mulligan, write a story inspired by the title, 'You never know what you will find'. Your story should have:

- – An interesting setting

- – A narrator

- – Two characters

- – An unanswered question.

Optional Rough Work

Study the Poster 'How Long Does Litter Last?' and complete the tasks which follow.

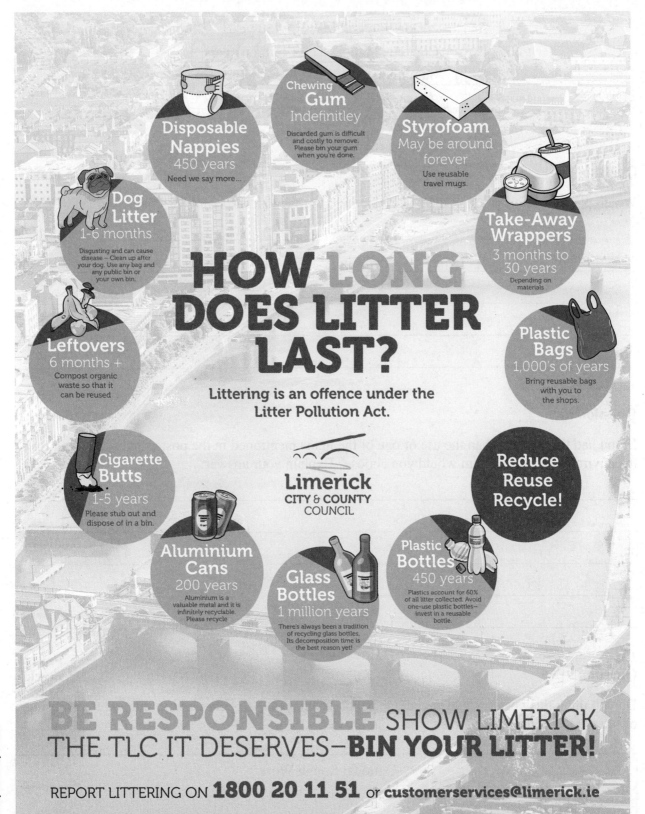

Question 6 (10 marks)

Using the information in the poster, write the correct letter (A, B, C, D, E) in the space on the right to show how long each item lasts.

A	Dog litter	450 years	
B	Cigarette butts	1 million years	
C	Aluminium cans	1–5 years	
D	Glass bottles	1–6 months	
E	Plastic bottles	200 years	

Question 7 (5 marks)

Which piece of information in the poster do you find the most surprising? Explain your answer.

_____

_____

_____

_____

_____

Question 8 (5 marks)

If you had the power to ban the use of one of the items mentioned in the poster, in order to improve the environment, which item would you choose? Explain your answer.

_____

_____

_____

_____

_____

Question 9 (15 marks)

Do you think this poster would encourage people to change their behaviour in relation to disposing of litter? Give three reasons to support your answer.

Optional Rough Work

212

Introduction

_____
_____
_____
_____
_____
_____

Reason 1 _____
_____
_____
_____
_____

Reason 2 _____
_____
_____
_____
_____

Reason 3 _____
_____
_____
_____
_____

Question 10 (30 marks)

(a) You are giving a talk to your class. The title is: *Be Responsible – Show Our Planet the Love It Deserves*. Which of the following images, A, B, or C, will you use as a background projection for your talk?

Reference Only

Image A

Image B

I would use Image _____.

(b) Explain your choice.

Optional Rough Work

(c) Suggest **two** ways you would liven up your oral presentation to make it as effective as possible.

Optional Rough Work

_____

_____

_____

_____

_____

_____

(d) Write the opening of your presentation. Be sure to catch the interest of your audience.

Optional Rough Work

_____

_____

_____

_____

_____

_____

216

Additional Writing Space. Label all work clearly with the question number and part.

NOTES

NOTES

NOTES

NOTES

NOTES

NOTES

NOTES

NOTES

NOTES

NOTES

NOTES

NOTES

NOTES

NOTES

NOTES

NOTES

Edco 2022/2023 School Year Planner

Calendar

SEPTEMBER: 1 Thurs, 2 Fri, 3 Sat, 4 Sun, 5 Mon, 6 Tues, 7 Wed, 8 Thurs, 9 Fri, 10 Sat, 11 Sun, 12 Mon, 13 Tues, 14 Wed, 15 Thurs, 16 Fri, 17 Sat, 18 Sun, 19 Mon, 20 Tues, 21 Wed, 22 Thurs, 23 Fri, 24 Sat, 25 Sun, 26 Mon, 27 Tues, 28 Wed, 29 Thurs, 30 Fri

OCTOBER: 1 Sat, 2 Sun, 3 Mon, 4 Tues, 5 Wed, 6 Thurs, 7 Fri, 8 Sat, 9 Sun, 10 Mon, 11 Tues, 12 Wed, 13 Thurs, 14 Fri, 15 Sat, 16 Sun, 17 Mon, 18 Tues, 19 Wed, 20 Thurs, 21 Fri, 22 Sat, 23 Sun, 24 Mon, 25 Tues, 26 Wed, 27 Thurs, 28 Fri, 29 Sat, 30 Sun, 31 Mon ●

NOVEMBER: 1 Tues ■, 2 Wed ■, 3 Thurs ■, 4 Fri ■, 5 Sat ◆, 6 Sun, 7 Mon, 8 Tues, 9 Wed, 10 Thurs, 11 Fri, 12 Sat, 13 Sun, 14 Mon, 15 Tues, 16 Wed, 17 Thurs, 18 Fri, 19 Sat, 20 Sun, 21 Mon, 22 Tues, 23 Wed, 24 Thurs, 25 Fri, 26 Sat, 27 Sun, 28 Mon, 29 Tues, 30 Wed

DECEMBER: 1 Thurs, 2 Fri, 3 Sat, 4 Sun, 5 Mon, 6 Tues, 7 Wed, 8 Thurs, 9 Fri, 10 Sat, 11 Sun, 12 Mon, 13 Tues, 14 Wed, 15 Thurs, 16 Fri, 17 Sat, 18 Sun, 19 Mon, 20 Tues, 21 Wed, 22 Thurs ■, 23 Fri ■, 24 Sat ■, 25 Sun ■, 26 Mon ●■, 27 Tues ■, 28 Wed ■, 29 Thurs ■, 30 Fri ■, 31 Sat ■

JANUARY: 1 Sun, 2 Mon ●, 3 Tues ■, 4 Wed ■, 5 Thurs, 6 Fri, 7 Sat, 8 Sun, 9 Mon, 10 Tues, 11 Wed, 12 Thurs, 13 Fri, 14 Sat, 15 Sun, 16 Mon, 17 Tues, 18 Wed, 19 Thurs, 20 Fri, 21 Sat, 22 Sun, 23 Mon, 24 Tues, 25 Wed, 26 Thurs, 27 Fri, 28 Sat, 29 Sun, 30 Mon, 31 Tues

FEBRUARY: 1 Wed ◆, 2 Thurs, 3 Fri, 4 Sat, 5 Sun, 6 Mon ●, 7 Tues, 8 Wed, 9 Thurs, 10 Fri, 11 Sat, 12 Sun, 13 Mon ■, 14 Tues ■, 15 Wed ■, 16 Thurs ■, 17 Fri ■, 18 Sat, 19 Sun, 20 Mon, 21 Tues, 22 Wed, 23 Thurs, 24 Fri, 25 Sat, 26 Sun, 27 Mon, 28 Tues

MARCH: 1 Wed, 2 Thurs, 3 Fri, 4 Sat, 5 Sun, 6 Mon, 7 Tues, 8 Wed, 9 Thurs, 10 Fri, 11 Sat, 12 Sun, 13 Mon, 14 Tues, 15 Wed, 16 Thurs, 17 Fri ●◆, 18 Sat, 19 Sun, 20 Mon, 21 Tues, 22 Wed, 23 Thurs, 24 Fri, 25 Sat, 26 Sun, 27 Mon, 28 Tues, 29 Wed, 30 Thurs, 31 Fri

APRIL: 1 Sat, 2 Sun, 3 Mon, 4 Tues, 5 Wed, 6 Thurs, 7 Fri, 8 Sat, 9 Sun, 10 Mon ●, 11 Tues ■, 12 Wed ■, 13 Thurs ■, 14 Fri ■, 15 Sat, 16 Sun, 17 Mon, 18 Tues, 19 Wed, 20 Thurs, 21 Fri, 22 Sat, 23 Sun, 24 Mon, 25 Tues, 26 Wed, 27 Thurs, 28 Fri, 29 Sat, 30 Sun

MAY: 1 Mon ●◆, 2 Tues, 3 Wed, 4 Thurs, 5 Fri, 6 Sat, 7 Sun, 8 Mon, 9 Tues, 10 Wed, 11 Thurs, 12 Fri, 13 Sat, 14 Sun, 15 Mon, 16 Tues, 17 Wed, 18 Thurs, 19 Fri, 20 Sat, 21 Sun, 22 Mon, 23 Tues, 24 Wed, 25 Thurs, 26 Fri, 27 Sat, 28 Sun, 29 Mon, 30 Tues, 31 Wed

JUNE: 1 Thurs, 2 Fri, 3 Sat, 4 Sun, 5 Mon ●, 6 Tues, 7 Wed ◆, 8 Thurs, 9 Fri, 10 Sat, 11 Sun, 12 Mon, 13 Tues, 14 Wed, 15 Thurs, 16 Fri, 17 Sat, 18 Sun, 19 Mon, 20 Tues, 21 Wed, 22 Thurs, 23 Fri, 24 Sat, 25 Sun, 26 Mon, 27 Tues, 28 Wed, 29 Thurs, 30 Fri

JULY: 1 Sat ◆, 2 Sun, 3 Mon, 4 Tues, 5 Wed, 6 Thurs, 7 Fri ◆, 8 Sat, 9 Sun, 10 Mon, 11 Tues, 12 Wed, 13 Thurs, 14 Fri, 15 Sat, 16 Sun, 17 Mon, 18 Tues, 19 Wed, 20 Thurs, 21 Fri, 22 Sat, 23 Sun, 24 Mon, 25 Tues, 26 Wed, 27 Thurs, 28 Fri, 29 Sat, 30 Sun, 31 Mon

AUGUST: 1 Tues, 2 Wed, 3 Thurs, 4 Fri, 5 Sat, 6 Sun, 7 Mon ●, 8 Tues, 9 Wed, 10 Thurs, 11 Fri, 12 Sat, 13 Sun, 14 Mon, 15 Tues, 16 Wed, 17 Thurs, 18 Fri, 19 Sat, 20 Sun, 21 Mon, 22 Tues, 23 Wed, 24 Thurs, 25 Fri, 26 Sat, 27 Sun, 28 Mon, 29 Tues, 30 Wed, 31 Thurs

FOR FREE ONLINE SOLUTIONS
visit www.e-xamit.ie